BEYOND

THE

BOUNDS OF HISTORY

Photo: "Cape Times"

BEYOND THE BOUNDS OF HISTORY

Scenes from the Old Stone Age

by

HENRI BREUIL

Membre de l'Institut de France
Professor of Prehistory at the Collège de France

English Translation
by
MARY E. BOYLE

Foreword
by
Field-Marshal J. C. SMUTS, P.C., C.H., K.C.

P. R. GAWTHORN, LTD

55 Russell Square, London, W.C.1

The photographs reproduced on pages 14, 24, 25, 27 and 29 were taken specially for this book by André Just and A. F. Kersting.

The maps were drawn by William Grimshaw and the decorations designed by Neave Parker.

FIRST PUBLISHED 1949.

World Copyright P. R. Gawthorn, Ltd.

Printed in Great Britain by EDSON (PRINTERS) LTD., LEAVESDEN, WATFORD, HERTS.

FOREWORD

*A*S I was in large measure responsible for initiating this publication, I may briefly explain the circumstances by way of introducing it to the public. While I was in Paris in 1946 in connection with the negotiations of the Peace Treaties with Italy and other countries I saw the Abbé Breuil on some matters in prehistory which interest us in common. Incidentally, he showed me some sketches he had made of scenes in pre-historic life as it might have existed in various parts of the world. I was deeply interested in these sketches, as the Abbé is not only our greatest living prehistorian, but is also a very competent draughtsman. I was struck by the educative and publicity value which such sketches could have for the general public who possess only the vaguest idea of what we already know about the appearance and ways of life of our prehistoric ancestors. I therefore suggested to the Abbé that he should consider the publication of these and similar sketches in prehistory.

In due course Mr. Percy R. Gawthorn—always ready to be helpful in publicising matters of popular scientific interest—was approached in regard to the idea. The result was this book, which I trust will prove welcome to all who are interested in the early and earliest phases of our human and pre-human past.

I know of no more enthralling story in science than that which the infant science of Prehistory has to tell. Here at last we pass beyond the bounds of history and establish contact with the most distant ancestors of our race. We see the most primitive roots and conditions from which the human race divine has grown into the mighty tree which now covers the face of this earth. We pass from the animal-like beginnings to the *highest developments of civilized man today. We witness a drama of advance to which science shows no parallel.*

It has been such a rapid advance. For the human race is still very young in the story of biological evolution and no one can foresee how far we shall yet travel if the pace is maintained and speeded up. Of all forms of life on this globe man has made the fastest and greatest progress. The latest comers have gone farthest in the race of life. If we look at pictures of plant life as may have existed before or in the earlier phases of, say, the Great Ice Age—such as may be found, for instance, in "Seward's Plant Life through the Ages"—we see comparatively little difference from the general appearance of plant life in our day. No doubt there have been greater changes in animal than in plant life during that period of some half a million years, but nothing like the enormous changes which have taken place in our human advance. Almost the whole span of our pre-human and human existence is covered in that comparatively brief geological period.

*C*OMPARING *the earliest Java and Pekin and Ipswich man of that age with modern man we see a march in evolution—anatomical and social —which is almost unbelievable in its speed and reach. The stages of this forced march are studied and revealed by the prehistorian. The evidence is still scant, but geological and biological progress is rapidly filling up the gaps. And we already have a fair general bird's-eye view of the scene covered by this advance. New methods and past discoveries help us to accelerate the pace at which our knowledge is accumulating. The immense gap before history is being filled out with more or less detailed, accurate knowledge. History itself assumes a new aspect in this wider setting. Our interest in our race and its story grows in the new perspective. And it is more than merely interest that is evoked. There is a message for us too, just as history has its message.*

For to me at least there is a very heartening message in prehistory.

FOREWORD

On that larger, truer time-scale we see a deeper meaning of our story than that which history conveys to us. On the time-scale of history which covers only a few thousand years we do not see much essential progress. Institutions change, forms of human life and existence change, but man himself remains much the same. Have we advanced beyond the Greeks of Homer's and Plato's day? Has the human soul changed since the Hebrew psalms were composed? Have we passed beyond the mental and spiritual stature of the men of two or three thousand years ago? Is man himself progressing, apart from the institutions he is developing in the course of history?

TO these questions what can our answers be? Man physically and spiritually seems almost to be standing still when our yardstick is history.

To see the true picture we have to take a larger time-scale. We have to call in the witness of prehistory. And then the answer is no longer in doubt. The progress physically, mentally and socially is almost beyond belief. Like Galileo we can now say in the light of prehistory: He is moving—man is advancing fundamentally. To those who have asked me whether I am a pessimist or an optimist I have replied that when I look merely at history I am tempted to be a pessimist about man, but when I look at prehistory I am an optimist. The case for progress on the evidence of prehistory is simply overwhelming.

For us, children of today, prehistory is therefore not only a matter of deep and absorbing interest, it is also a message—a call to good cheer and faith in our future, an inspiration for the march, the endless march and the road stretching before us.

ILLUSTRATIONS TO THE INTRODUCTION

Page

Letter from the Author to his Father, 1897 . . . 13

Seminary Garden: St. Sulpice, Paris 14

At the entrance of the Peers Cave, Cape Province . 17

Copying Cave Paintings: Brandberg Mountains . . 19

Rose Cottage Cave: Ladybrand, O.F.S. . . . 19

Cave Shelters at Chou-Kou-Tien 20

Site of Cro-du-Charnier, near Solutré 23

Entrance to the Tuc d'Audoubert: Ariège . .24 & 25

Entrance to Sanctuary of Trois Frères: Ariège . 27

Cavern of Mas d'Azil: Ariège 29

INTRODUCTION

IN presenting this collection of sketches of our ancestors in the Old Stone Age to the public, I feel that I should explain how they came to be made, since they are so far removed from my usually much more serious work.

From my very early childhood the study of Nature had an unconquerable attraction for me and I turned instinctively towards it. A taste for keen observation and a searching curiosity led me first towards the study of Insects (Entomology). From my earliest years my father, whom I accompanied on his walks, amused himself by collecting Coleoptera. The trunk of an old rotten willow tree, inside which we found two specimens of *Elater sanguineus,* the most beautiful of our click-beetles ; the capture on the trunk of a poplar of a ground beetle (*Calosoma inquisitor*) ; on an oak tree which had been felled, of a whole tribe of biting *Rhagium* and of *Clytia*, coloured like wasps ; or on the flexible twigs of an osier of the beautiful *Aromia moschata* (musk-beetle) with its long goat horns, are my chief recollections of moments of strong, exciting emotion. Then I extended my interest to butterflies, catching my first Swallow-tail (*Papilio machaon*) in a field of lucerne; the discovery of a poplar " Dead Leaf " on the cornice of an old wall; the care of strange, beautiful caterpillars—of that of the Puss moth, or the Privet Hawk moth—what marvellous childhood thrills of pure joy these names bring back to me !

My father, except for his collection of insects, was nothing of a naturalist. It was a very humble schoolmaster, Monsieur Paul André, the son-in-law of my grandfather's gamekeeper, who first spoke to me of geology during his and my holidays in Soissonais, showing me moulds of the interior of giant Cerithiums preserved in the coarse Eocene limestone. In those days these were dated from the time of the Flood, but they gave me a deep, though no doubt vague impression, of a past so very far away that I could hardly imagine it.

In Prehistory I had already been struck by two things. The worthy schoolmaster at Clermont, Monsieur Devimeux, who was the first person to whom I announced my election to the Collège de France in later years, taught me the rudiments of knowledge in his private lessons, from the time I was seven to ten years old. One day he gave me to read aloud the description of the discovery of a Neolithic burial and the site of Aurignac. I did not properly understand what this meant till much later, but the fact that I remember it shows that I was not deaf to the call of those mysterious Stone Ages. I already knew of their existence, for on wet days in the Soissonais country, where my mother's parents lived, my grandmother allowed me to open her showcase, into which I often gazed, and gently handle some polished axes—Pressigny knives and one Levallois flake (the latter not much esteemed), that the plough had turned up in the clay of the neighbouring fields. Naturally, all these objects were to her and to me, Celtic or Gaulish. But Humanity's long past opened before me and I began to dream. There was no one near me to teach me more.

The month of August spent in Picardy often brought me to the Château of Bouillancourt-en-Sery where, under the roof, there was an attic in which I was often allowed to rummage, and it was there I discovered a small collection of rocks and fossils. I was instinctively fascinated and began to ask many questions of a distinguished geologist from Abbeville, d'Ault de Mesnil, a family friend. More than once he went to the attic with me and, amused by my curiosity, answered me as well as he could. Although I understood very little, it gave me a new world, with an ocean peopled by Ichthyosaurus, Plesiosaurus, Ammonites and Belemnites.

I began to collect strange stones myself, silicified cerithiums from soft chalk beds, shark teeth from the Lutetian level ; a mammoth tooth from the Saint Médard gravels was for long the finest ornament of my small collection. Again, instinctively, I added to these a series of skulls of vermin, trapped by my grandfather's gamekeeper, and these, I own, gave me my first and very valuable introduction to comparative osteology.

When I had passed my school certificate, d'Ault, whom I met every summer, sent me to collect fossils in the green chalk at Nesle near Blangy ; he also showed me some deerhorn picks found near Bouillancourt in a pit from which the Neolithic people extracted flint. I began to realize more fully the long past of geological and prehistoric times, but insects were always my first love and the blue wings of a Morpho in the Desmonville Museum at Abbeville held for me ever the same magic.

I must confess that my artistic education was never the outcome of study in a well-known studio. The ten to sixteen-year-old schoolboy that I was learnt to sharpen his pencils or charcoal and laboriously to blacken a sheet of paper, copying some print or cast. He much preferred sketching according to his fancy, hens, ducks, dogs and cows at harvest time on his aunt's farm in Picardy, where she made butter and delicious cakes which were washed down with cider. The gaining of his " bachot " (school certificate) earned the longed-for shooting licence, and his pencil recorded the movements of rabbits, hares, partridges and pheasants living on his maternal grandfather's property near Soissons. His grandmother had been a good pupil of Justin Louvrié, and sometimes gave him a few hints. A keen entomologist, sometimes a botanist, the young student often drew with a certain facility, butterflies, coleoptera and wild flowers ; but he was never more than a mediocre water-colourist.

Somewhat later, it must be admitted that he devoted his energies to drawing uncharitable portraits of the inspiring profiles of some of his professors, or to illustrating satirically the archaic descriptions in the pious biographies which lulled him during his meals in the refectory. Certain professors of ethics, who made quick eloquent gestures, involuntarily taught him to sketch characteristic attitudes rapidly.

Then towards 1900 —and ever since—the neophyte prehistorian began the unending work which during several months every year led him to decipher and copy the engravings and frescoes in the Reindeer Age caves. The teachings of this hard school lasted for nearly fifty years, during which the schoolboy of 1890, the seminarist of 1895-1900, had to learn all alone, and with makeshift materials, techniques and ways of working inspired by his models, familiarize himself with the "feeling" of these old masters—the hunters

Letter from the author to his Father, dated 3rd January, 1897; the decorations show an early interest in botany and entomology.

13

Garden of the seminary of St. Sulpice in Paris where the author learned his first words of English. It is now open to the public.

of reindeer, mammoth and bison. These were, in fact, his only Masters, nearly all of them purely animal painters. But after 1908 the enthusiastic student spent many months looking at the Art of the Eastern Spanish caves where there were rock frescoes of frenzied hunting and war scenes in which gesticulation played an important part.

Visits to many of the most celebrated museums of Europe, where the public can study the finest work of ancient sculptors and classic painters, awoke in this pupil of the great Masters of the Stone Age a fervent but very eclectic interest in all creations of human art throughout the ages. And thus, little by little, the background was formed which was to produce the drawings in this book.

★   ★   ★   ★

From Fossil Man I had learnt to sketch animals and people from memory, without correction ; often during banquets at scientific congresses I decorated my neighbours' menu cards with bison in silhouette, or other prehistoric beasts, and sometimes there was great competition for these.

The last world war drove me into exile, first at Lisbon, then in South Africa, and I was so warmly welcomed in both these places that I was able to continue my researches on fresh ground. Having no other means of showing my gratitude to kind foreign colleagues or hospitable friends, it sometimes happened that I tried to draw some scene recalling an episode of those far-off times to the study of which I had devoted my life. Occasionally I felt that I was successful.

In December, 1944, the South African summer induced us to wait till the sun was less strong before setting off for the bushveld sites and dongas, and our work was reduced to the daily study of the material we had gathered in the preceding months. Tired by the excessive altitude of the Rand, my faithful fellow-worker, Miss M. E. Boyle, who had accompanied me to these southern limits of the Old World, went for some weeks' rest to the orange orchards on a lower level at Rustenburg. Meanwhile my own work at the Archæological Survey left me free in the early morning and after supper. It was then that the idea occurred to me to amuse myself by again trying to make sketches of prehistoric life. At week-ends, when I always went to see Dr. Grasset and his family who were to us like our own family, I showed these efforts to entertain my hosts, whose manifest interest encouraged me.

A drawing of a bison hunt, done for Mrs. Diana Dent in gratitude for a small service, was framed and hung in her drawing-room, where, if I may say so, it looked rather well. (A reproduction of this sketch will be found on page 64.) One day two children visiting the house climbed up on the sofa so as to see the picture better.

" This is drawn by a great artist, isn't it ? The bison is so frightened,

Beyond the Bounds of History

I can see it in his eyes," said the boy. He had re-acted to the violent atmosphere that I had tried to give to the struggle between the hunter and his quarry. This sincere homage from unprejudiced children impressed me greatly. Instead of sketching, as I had been doing, on no matter what piece of white paper, I had now, in obedience to my friends, to use more costly sheets which they made an effort to find for me. I then set out in my early mornings and evenings to draw a series of small pictures showing the stages of development of Fossil Man and his civilizations. Begun at Christmas, 1944, this work was interrupted in the beginning of February by a fresh departure for the south coast where I studied the ancient sea levels and their relation to the different chipped stone industries. Since then I have had neither the leisure nor peace of mind to return to my drawings.

To the children, to the adolescents, I dedicate these. Perhaps, judging by what I have seen, some grown-up people may also take pleasure in them? We certainly owe that much to the children. Was it not the little five-year-old girl of Marcelino de Sautuola who, in 1879, whilst her father was digging in the floor of the cave of Altamira (Santander, Spain), was the first to see the great and magnificent frescoes on the roof, greeting them with a cry of "Bulls! Bulls!" (Toros! Toros!)? Although it is true that she now remembers nothing about it!

Was it not the band of lads at Montignac (Dordogne), led by Ravidat and Marsal, who slipped through a narrow shaft into the Hall of the Great Bulls, on the 12th September, 1940, and thus were the first to see and understand the incredible frescoes of Lascaux (though their first emotion was fear)?

Was it not the three young sons of Count Begouën who, whilst exploring wide dark corridors in 1912-14, had the incomparable luck of finding one after the other the clay bisons of the Tuc d'Audoubert (Ariège) and the neighbouring sanctuary of the Trois Frères, with its horned God looking down on hundreds of admirable engravings?

It is, therefore, to the children and adolescents and those older people who have known how to preserve their freshness of soul and imagination that I dedicate these modest efforts. May they inspire some among them to become explorers or prehistorians! Without the teaching of schoolmaster Laval, Marsal and Ravidat would certainly not have understood what a marvel of art was Lascaux.

But I also dedicate my pictures to my oldest Masters, the Fossil Men themselves. I have in truth lived a great deal with them, whether picturing them on the gravel terraces of the Garonne, the Somme, the Thames and the Vaal, or on the raised beaches of Portugal, Morocco and Cape Province, or scratching in the ashes of their hearths in the rock-shelters of the Dordogne

The author at the entrance to the Peers Cave at Fishhoek, Cape Province.
Photo : " Cape Times."

and the Pyrenees, or in the bone brecchias of Chou-Kou-Tien (China) and Makapan in the Transvaal ; everywhere their chipped stone tools or the bones they broke or used spoke to me of them.

Sometimes, in the course of long hours of copying their frescoes and engravings in the dark corridors of Niaux and Trois Frères in the Pyrenees and La Pileta, near Malaga, I rested for a short time from my hard task and let my mind and eyes roam round those halls where, in the days when they were painted, mysterious rites certainly took place. The solemn silence of the present then seemed to be broken by the shouts and chants of the officiating heads or the initiates, giving vent in these echoing halls to cries of fear, joy and hope as, in their animal masks or sacred nudity, they performed dramatic pantomimes embodying tribal traditions before the awe-struck novices. To these men, perhaps the most splendid of our ancestors, whose souls certainly thrilled to the deep emotions engendered by the first great Art, I dedicate, almost in a filial spirit, these pages which they have inspired.

When turning over my pictures my young readers, who are not specialists, will wish to give a more or less definite date to the various stages in human development in which the Scenes are placed, and I must in a very brief way endeavour to satisfy their curiosity.

It was Edouard Lartet who first classified the French prehistoric sites. From the start the study of Prehistory was essentially French, partly because of the nationality of the chief savants in its early days and partly because of the classic sites, the names of which were used, then as now, to denote the successive civilizations of prehistoric times in Europe. Thus Abbevillian denotes the oldest set of tools and civilization amongst animals which have died out or emigrated, the first signs of which were found near Abbeville. The later tools and civilization, called Acheulean, were first revealed at St. Acheul (Somme) ; Levalloisian from Levallois (Paris) ; Mousterian from Le Moustier (Dordogne) ; Aurignacian from Aurignac (Haute Garonne) ; Solutrean from Solutré (Saône et Loire) ; Magdalenian from La Madeleine (Dordogne) ; Azilian from Mas d'Azil (Ariège) ; Tardenoisean from La-Fère-en-Tardenois (Aisne).

To these I added Clactonian from Clacton-on-Sea (England)—which comes just before the Acheulean ; the Levalloisian, quoted above, and Tayacian from Tayac (Dordogne). Once the geographical sites are grasped these titles lose their ponderous elaboration.

This classification cannot be generalized even over Europe without important regional modifications, but it remains true that our northern France and southern England, which once formed a single country, contain the finest classic sites of the three most ancient civilizations. Moreover, the four subsequent ones were most richly represented by that brilliant artistic civilization of the

In the Brandberg Mountains, S.W. Africa, the author copies a cave painting while his assistant, Miss Mary Boyle, describes it in writing.

Photo: Dr. Ernst R. Scherz

At work in Rose Cottage Cave (right), *near Ladybrand, O.F.S., with Mr. B. Malan of the Archæological Survey of Witwatersrand University.*

reindeer hunters, cave painters and sculptors of statuettes in our Aquitaine and its natural extension, Cantabria.

However long ago Man appeared on the Earth, he is the latest arrival amongst all the inhabitants ; when he first made his presence evident, the oceans had already swarmed with living creatures for more than 500 million years. We find land animals and green plants in soil some 10 million years younger. The vertebrates, the first of which were Fish, are about 300 million years old ; amphibious Batracians come next at 285 million years ; then the Reptiles at 270 million years—though their great development into gigantic creatures only took place later when the oldest known Mammal appeared,

Entrance to the cave shelters of Chou-Kou-Tien, the home of generations of Pekin Man. (See page 35.)
Photo: Carnegie Institution of Washington.

a type of little shrew (field mouse), 160 million years ago ; and the forerunners of birds which evolved from Reptiles 120 million years ago. It it only about 80 million years ago that Mammals began to multiply and to branch out from the central group into those we know as carnivorous or grazing animals, rodents, and tiny little lemurs, the forerunners of Apes : this was 30 million years ago.

As yet there were no Men, only small creatures heralding the Apes which were developing only in the Old World. Certain groups of these, " Dryopithecus," accentuated various characteristics during several tens of million years before there are definite signs of Man, though these characteristics show us that they were the advance guard of Man. Some, chiefly in central and tropical Africa and in the Siwalik Hills of northern India, developed an almost human set of teeth, a bigger brain and sometimes an upright attitude. These were not Men, however, though they resembled them, but Apes, doubtless not very different in behaviour from the Chimpanzees and Gorillas of today. We now begin to perceive the dawn or slow arrival of Man which lasted as far as we can judge for about two or three million years—attempts at a human type, most of which came to nothing and did not survive.

One day people noticed that all over the Old World—in Asia, Europe and Africa, but mostly in warm regions, from Pekin to Java and western Europe—there had been beings who had chipped stone into tools or weapons, using as well bones and deerhorn and perhaps wood (though that has perished), and who had captured Fire and maintained it, without perhaps knowing how to make it. Physically, though they were two-legged, they were not very different from the highest Apes, which I have already mentioned, but their brains were much bigger ; they had feet upon which they could walk and human hands which, guided by an ingenious mind, began to make tools. For these reasons, they were Men, or at least, a kind of Man. They must have had some way of talking ; they hunted and ate the flesh of their quarry, breaking the bones and skulls of their victims so as to eat the marrow and brains, and seemingly had a sort of worship of the skulls of their dead relatives. What they thought, even supposing that they did think in our own fashion, we do not know.

About this time the climate, for astronomical reasons, changed in regions not far away from the North and South Poles. There were heavy rains in the regions now tropical, and in the temperate zones and farther north, snowfalls led to the development of huge ice-fields. The ocean, deprived by this vast frozen area of much water which the sun had sucked up from it and which had not been returned, sank considerably, leaving uncovered and dry land-bridges which are today under the sea.

Tribes of Men, descendants of the preceding ones or of others we do not yet know, lived in the time of these great changes which obliged the animals, who liked a warm climate, to emigrate southwards. But, though life was hard, several tribes remained on the edge of the big ice-fields. In some of these their ancestral brutal appearance was exaggerated, as we see by remains found at Mauer (Baden, Germany) ; others were already trying to get rid of this appearance and become more like the Men of today, as is shown by the remains found at Piltdown (Sussex, England), but in spite of the progress in their brains and skulls they retained the jaw and canine teeth of a Chimpanzee. This happened during and between the first, second and third extensions of the ice in northern Europe.

As the fourth Ice Age drew near, those races most brutal in appearance, such as that known as Neanderthal, prevailed in Europe and there they lived during the first half of this period, hunting mammoths, rhinoceros, great cave bear, wild horses and cattle and reindeer. They took refuge in rock-shelters or caves. These Men lived from 187,000 to 70,000 B.C. Certain ways of burial, as well as the worship of skulls, are the only signs we have that their thought reached beyond the present life ; Death, like Life, was therefore a problem to them.

It was only during the second half of the last Ice Age, after 70,000 B.C., that different groups of human beings like present-day Men appeared in Europe. They lived as hunters, like their predecessors, whom they no doubt killed off like animals. But the life of the individual, as the life of the race, grew complicated ; there are signs of commerce, of the division of labour, of very advanced specialization in the working of stone, or bone—anything wooden has perished. Thanks to the graves and various somewhat involved rites in which red ochre—symbol of life—played a significant part, we know that they ornamented themselves with shells and pierced teeth made into necklaces or bracelets, or artistically arranged and sewn on to their fur garments and hoods. The cold in winter made this warm apparel absolutely necessary and, from a certain date, bone needles with eyes were made for the purpose of sewing these skin clothes together.

Javelins no doubt replaced primitive spears, and these were soon hurled by a throwing stick. These weapons in turn were later replaced by bows and arrows. Sharp stone points, cleverly made, were given to the arrows, or there were deerhorn, bone or ivory darts, sometimes decorated with figures or ornamental patterns, for these newcomers were also admirable artists. The oldest of their works were small female figures of ivory or stone ; subsequently they fashioned animals.

Later still they made, in mass, freehand drawings on small objects, some on small flat stones or bone flakes or hunting amulets. But long before this art of " miniatures " developed, they had learnt to trace animal silhouettes on the walls of caves—probably places where there were sacred ceremonies. These were mostly of the beasts they hunted, more rarely of imaginary or composite animals—semi-human creatures, their heads usually covered by an animal or grotesque mask. The use of hunting disguises led to the wearing of ceremonial masks which were supposed to have magic power. Thus, if these people wished to represent spiritual beings, or even God, He or they were disguised as powers controlling the animal world.

We see all this in the engravings, bas-reliefs and paintings which are sometimes remarkably perfect and of gigantic size ; one bull in the cave of Lascaux is about eighteen feet long. The painting technique blossomed out at different

Limestone cliffs near Solutré, at the foot of which is the celebrated site of Cro-du-Charmer.
Photo : Hélène Balfet.

stages and in cycles ; there were two outstanding periods with intervals of lesser achievement between.

These invaders, therefore, evolved somewhere towards the East or South-East, whilst their predecessors carried on and intensified the physical characteristics and elementary civilization of early times. The newcomers quickly suppressed the degenerate remains of an older humanity, but of the origin of these invaders, who were certainly our direct ancestors, we know nothing. When we meet them in Europe they are already mature and of varied type, with a civilization which has passed its early stages, but which they ceaselessly

The River Volp leaving the limestone cavern of Tuc d'Audoubert at

Montesquieu-Avantès in the Province of Ariège, France. (*See page 79.*)

improved. Waves of them followed each other during the last thirty thousand years before our era, each wave bringing fresh elements which mingled with the first, each sharing in the evolution of this steadily developing civilization.

The reign of these people—brilliant hunters, lovers of art and adventure, nomads and, in their own way, religious and thinkers—lasted as long as the Ice Age fauna remained in our Western world, that is to say until about 10,000 B.C.

But other branches of the same races, deep in what are now the Asiatic steppes and African deserts, having discovered pastoral life, laboriously collected flocks and herds ; whilst yet others found out how to cultivate plants yielding food and textiles. These peoples had partially blended before they were driven from their original steppes by drought which brought them daily nearer famine. They started marching westwards towards the lands where forests and meadows had gained on the " tundras " and " barren grounds " of the last glacial era.

Pushing before them the weak Mediterranean and Baltic tribes who were better at gathering shell-fish than at hunting, they absorbed the more gifted races devoted to big game hunting. Setting out, perhaps 25,000 years ago from their original birthplace, they reached, step by step, our part of the world and were the first to start Agriculture. They built the first fortified cities and armed themselves to protect their harvests, both of flocks and grain. This took place between 10,000 and 5,000 B.C., according to the regions.

Then, in the Near East, the dawn of written history broke, our Europe was established and the peoples whom we know settled there, forming the base of the present nations. Not one of them remembers the very distant past, the alternating advances and retreats of the glaciers during many thousands of years, or the migrations of warm or cold-loving animals, or the tribes which lived upon them.

Some half symbolical legends, preserved by shepherds, were all that retained a few confused echoes of the most recent of these far-off days in which the first type of Man, armed with flints and surrounded by gigantic monsters, blazed the trail to the Empire of Humanity.

All that—the deserts, first fertile, then sterile ; the seas which swelled upward for about three hundred feet and then sank to double that amount, leaving coasts, archipelagos or land-bridges, first high and dry and afterwards submerged—all that, no one remembers exactly, although until the discovery of Agriculture at least 15,000 years ago in the East it was the terrifying setting to life for almost a million years.

Less than two centuries ago the big fossil bones of elephants were still thought to be those of the semi-legendary heroes of proto-historic times.

Entrance to the Sanctuary of Trois Frères at Montesquieu-Avantès. (*See page* 79.)

Beyond the Bounds of History

At Hoxne in Suffolk, in 1797, John Frere was the first to declare their animal nature and their association with pointed stone axes made by Man—a detail already observed in 1690 by Conyers in London, although he believed that they belonged to the days of Cæsar. John Frere never stopped trying to rouse scientific societies from their torpor on the subject. But it was not until 1847 and onwards that the repeated announcements of his discoveries near Abbeville by Boucher de Perthes brought about a change in learned opinions. It was the tenacity of this literary and philosophical genius which, in 1858-1859, induced the visit and control by English savants—Falconer, Prestwick and John Evans—who, with the celebrated geologist, Charles Lyell, certified the accuracy of his claims. A few months later scientific opinion altered, and Prehistory was born and developed by giant strides.

Not until less than 100 years ago did Humanity come to possess solid proof of its unbelievable age, of the numberless generations through which its physical and ethical types were established ; the silent stages during which Fire was first harnessed ; then stone-chipping learnt ; and then, much later, the art of sculpture and the engraving and painting of living beings. What a marvellous romance, surpassing in its reality all the imaginative dreams of Jules Verne and H. G. Wells !

Is there any problem, any subject, freer from the gloom of present-day history, on which to exercise our imagination or that of our children ? Anything farther removed from our economic and social worries ? Anything more encouraging of hope in the distant future, than this History of Man in which the Age of Fire takes the place of our Age of Atomic Force ?

In the beginning, when Man used Fire incautiously, he must many times have set his straw hut alight, or the dry grass of the steppes, or the forest, before he learnt to control it and use it judiciously. Paying dearly in this way, he discovered how to use Fire as his chief protection against wild beasts, making it serve kitchen and forge and the family hearth where he warmed his limbs. Is not this very much like what is now happening to us with the terrible atomic power, as yet hardly discovered ?

In truth, though almost a million years old, Humanity is still in its infancy ; after this short phase of three or four thousand years of written history it has still a long road to travel, doubtless longer than those forgotten childish years, the history of which prehistorians search for in the ancient sea-beaches, river terraces and dark caves.

May Humanity at last see the victory of Peace, thanks to a parallel development on the spiritual side of Thought and Ethics. May the contemplation of this long, splendid and laborious Past be a comfort and refuge to my young readers, amidst the turmoil of the Present. May it create serenity by showing

Southern entrance of the cavern of Mas d' Azil in the province of Ariège, France. (*See page 68.*)

to each of us how humble is our position and bring the hope of a juster, truer human order, in which the conquests of the Soul and the Ideal will equal those of Physical Force and its application to Industry.

★   ★   ★   ★

In the concluding pages of this introduction, I would like to concentrate the essence of my study as to what, in my opinion, is the type of mind needed in every scientific worker, and which I should like to see possessed by any of my young friends who wish to devote their lives to Science.

The first essential for all scientific work is to have the *spirit of curiosity*. As my friend Miles Burkitt has said : " Man is an animal who busies himself about what does not concern him "—that is to say what is beyond the immediate material life. Every Man worthy of the name has this gift of curiosity which his individual talents guide into different channels ; it is absolutely indispensable for an archæologist, above all for a prehistorian, who must be a naturalist and must study to try to understand natural phenomena and deposits and the different techniques of fossil human production.

If this curiosity is to be fruitful it must be seriously concentrated on a small number of subjects, for Life is too short to follow many. It is better to dig a few deep furrows than to scratch a wide surface superficially and uselessly.

But to balance this *spirit of limitation* the interests must be broad, including not only those sciences closely associated with the one selected, but—within bounds—a wide human culture, bringing repose by the joy of Art and of the Mind. The mind will be all the fresher to return to its task ; it will have gained in language, expression and even conception, fresh inspiration and discoveries and ever greater gifts of observation.

Do you not see better when, if your eyes are tired by gazing too intently, you rest them by looking elsewhere and then turn back again refreshed by other visions ? It is not only at the beginning of our lives that we should circumscribe our efforts, but also later, when there is a mass of work. Consider as your duty only that which another cannot do, or do as well if he were in your place. If, after you have started a subject, you find someone on your road who is able, or better able, than you to work at it, hand him the task joyfully—there will be one less load on your shoulders.

To understand physical facts you must possess the *spirit of analysis* ; to master them you must not only look at them steadily, but touch objects with your fingers so as to be able to dissect them and follow their complex processes. Natural and physical facts evade a rapid glance. The analyst, therefore, requires a *spirit of tenacity*—a capacity for obstinate effort, an untiring patience which is never beaten or satisfied. He needs to have an *unprejudiced spirit*, an unselfish spirit, searching for the truth only, and although forced to work on a theory, not seeking to prove his own theories right, for their very failure is no less enlightening than the new problems that they suggest.

This love of effort would be no more than a sporting attitude if it did not lead to new outlooks. To analyse is well, but you must then co-ordinate your material. Observations drawn from the soil tend to develop synthetic explanations—new halting-places from which the mind starts off to plunge ahead beyond them.

To succeed in this you must have the *spirit of meditation*, both active and passive in turn. As bodily health requires a happy balance of endocrine secretions giving opposite results, so you must sometimes definitely concentrate your thought, chewing the cud, if I may say so, of accumulated observations and, on occasion, leaving the reins to Nature who is extraordinarily clever at handling them. During expeditions, hours spent in the garden, in fishing, shooting or other human diversions, you must *let yourself think*.

Thought then travels in the subconscious and returns more complete, sometimes rich in new suggestions and inspirations which should be seized at once and controlled in their turn. It is here that both Audacity and Prudence play their part. Prudence must be exercised to try to keep in mind the various aspects of reality which are always complex. Certain of these aspects, which you may not have noted, will be immediately grasped by other minds. But having done that, Audacity claims its rights and must give you Courage and true independence of thought. Once the elements of a problem have been conscientiously studied, the time comes to take your bearings. Once you have studied these elements as much, or more, than any living soul, no attention should be paid to established opinion or accepted theories. You must march straight forward leaving those behind you, without bothering whether you please or displease, not because you wish to call attention to yourself by opposition but because the facts you have carefully observed lead you to move forward.

Opposition for its own sake springs from a sterile form of mind posing as critical and it leads to nothing. The searcher will always meet some of this on his road, either because envy slips in or because his ideas upset habits of thought which had become embedded in an agreeable indolence. Under the plea of a love of truth and inspired more by caution than by hard work, this false spirit of criticism, though itself incapable of interpretation, construction and discovery, is usually expressed in a wordy report or much conveniently vague humming and hawing. You must be indifferent to all criticism not founded on a serious examination of the facts. He who has not observed may talk well, but his words are without value.

On the other hand, you must be open, attentive and even sympathetic to all criticism coming from conscientious people who have seriously and directly examined the subject, especially if their training is somewhat different from yours and is likely to have given them a type of experience which you may lack. Such criticism gives you a chance to profit by their knowledge and to control, complete or reform your own point of view.

Do not bemoan such differences of opinion. Criticism, even if unjust, spurs on to more perfect work he who does not lose time in disputing with vain words. All personal controversy is a waste of time and strength, except when the scientific world must be enlightened about spurious work and the truth vindicated. The searcher has better use to make of the limited time he is given.

As for looters, you will have crowds of them if your work is worth while. Let them alone—the things they borrow from you will popularize your discoveries and pay homage to their value.

You will also meet sincere, hard-working, intelligent colleagues, most of them young individualists who think that they will attain conclusions other than yours. If, as frequently happens, they are clever at self-development when brought face to face with facts—and they may have observed some which had not occurred to you—welcome them with an open mind, try to follow their reasoning and in exchange tell them what they may not have noted in yours. And, when doing so, do not pride yourself on having any authority but in a knowledge of the facts ; be very careful that from being "a sign-post pointing out the good road to take," you do not become "a barrier falling across the path." Till our last days we should remain, like Emile Cartailhac, an "old student," and the young will help us to do this.

You will find that your initial differences will often dissolve of their own accord. The young will show you certain new results obtained by their efforts, extending and correcting those you have secured ; while the experience you have gained will shorten for them the road which it cost you so much to find. More than once you will gain a friend, proud to have been understood and to understand you better. These will be they who, having taken the divine torch from your trembling hands—the flame of "knowing more and better each day"—will light in the near future and, after your day, the spiritual course of Humanity.

SCENES
FROM THE
OLD STONE AGE

CONTENTS

Scene   *Page*

1   THE HUNTERS' RETURN AT CHOU-KOU-TIEN 35
2   CHIPPING FLINT IN THE OLD PALÆOLITHIC DAYS—N.W. EUROPE . 38
3   WORKING AND TRIMMING DOLERITE ON BANKS OF THE VAAL . 41
4   ATTACKING A SHE-BEAR IN HER DEN 42
5   HUNTING BISON 43
6   HUNTING THE CERVUS MEGACEROS 47
7   MAMMOTH HUNTING IN ANCIENT PALÆOLITHIC TIMES IN DORDOGNE 47
8   WILD HORSES ATTACKED BY LIONS 50
9   MAMMOTHS VISIT A MAGDALENIAN ROCK SHELTER . 51
10 FLINT CHIPPING IN UPPER PALÆOLITHIC TIMES . . . 54
11 WORKING BONE AND DEERHORN IN MAGDALENIAN TIMES . 55
12 THE PREPARATION OF SKINS 57
13 A NATURAL CIRCUS IN UPPER PALÆOLITHIC DAYS . . 58
14 SALMON RUNNING 60
15 PASSAGE OF THE REINDEER IN THE AUTUMN . . 63
16 BIG GAME HUNTING WHICH BROUGHT FORTH GREAT ART . 63
17 ALPINE SPORTS IN THE REINDEER AGE 65
18 SCULPTORS AT WORK IN THE ROCK-SHELTER OF CAP BLANC . 66
19 MAGDALENIAN FUNERAL CEREMONY 71
20 WILD CATTLE CROSSING A WIDE RIVER 71
21 A MODEL POSES FOR AN AURIGNACIAN SCULPTOR . 72
22 TRADING WITH ORNAMENTAL SHELLS 73
23 HUNTING DISGUISES AND DRAWING FROM LIFE IN MAGDALENIAN
      TIMES 77
24 GRINDING OCHRE AND PAINTING FRESCOES ON ROCK . 77
25 THE SANCTUARY OF TROIS FRÈRES AT MONTESQUIEU-AVANTÈS. 79
26 PALÆOLITHIC ROCK PAINTERS OF EASTERN SPAIN . . 83
27 THE SHELL-FISH EATERS OF THE SEA SHORE . . 86
28 THE AZILIANS AT MAS D'AZIL 88
29 RED DEER HUNTING IN MESOLITHIC DAYS . . . 91
30 HUNTING ELK IN SOUTH SCANDINAVIA IN THE MESOLITHIC EPOCH 91
31 MESOLITHIC SETTLEMENTS NEAR THE MOUTH OF THE TAGUS 92

Chart: GLACIATIONS & HUMAN INDUSTRIES & RACES IN EUROPE . 96
      INDEX 97

SCENE ONE

The Hunters' Return at Chou-Kou-Tien

CHOU-KOU-TIEN, sixty miles south of Pekin, is in a gorge at the edge of the high Mongolian plateau bordering the great plain of Pekin; through this gorge a stream flows down to the plain. In the Silurian chalk hills, forming an anti-clinal, a large rock-shelter was produced by many recurring falls of rock, and successive generations of Pekin Man, a human type closely related to the *Pithecanthropus* of Java, lived there for many thousands of years.

Here we see a tribe busy with their various occupations in a corner of the rock-shelter. Three hunters are returning from an expedition, one bearing a young Deer; another the heavy antlers of a great Stag of the group of European Megaceros. The Chief carries only his weapons—a wooden stake, the horn of a Gazelle and a dagger made from the antler of a young Stag; his two companions do not possess such daggers. The hunters are greeted on the threshold of the rock-shelter by the Chief's wife and child.

In the shelter itself, the Woman on the right is splitting a block of quartz by " bi-polar percussion " ; a pile of split pieces lies near. She is striking the block with a pebble which has a depression in the centre made by the repeated blows; flakes already struck off and more pebbles with cups caused in the same way lie beside the boulder which serves her as an anvil. On her right, a Man is trimming flakes, also partly by bi-polar technique, which he is fashioning into end-scrapers, points, knives or chisels. Slightly behind and to the left, another Pekin Man is cutting a Deer antler in pieces with a sharp stone. These pieces will be used, the tines as daggers, the thicker parts as hammers or handles.

On the extreme left in the immediate foreground, a reserve of pebbles picked up in the stream is laid out in two rough circles within which is a number of wide split pieces of bone (several trimmed by percussion), heads of long bones with an epiphysis that have been trimmed to make points or chisels, and pieces of deerhorn fashioned into clubs and daggers. There are, also, a Gazelle horn to be made into a dagger, and jaw-bones of a big wild Boar or Deer used for different purposes. To the right of the pebble circles are the antlers and ribs of a large type of Deer and a little heap of Gazelle horns, none of which has yet been adapted for use. Next to these are some horn shafts, with only

35

their branches struck off, and several wooden pikes ; we must conclude that the latter existed, but no wood has been preserved.

The couple on the left of the group in the shelter are making fire. The Man first produces a spark by friction while the Woman holds out a tuft of dry grass and leaves to catch it. She will then carry it to the hearth which is between them surrounded by small pebbles. Behind them, another fire burns brightly, cooking a joint of Wild Boar. A Woman is keeping the flames going, while her companion and a child are warming themselves ; a heap of twigs nearby will provide more fuel. The enormous mass of ash discovered in the

excavations at Chou-Kou-Tien leaves no doubt of the intensive use of fire, but we cannot tell whether Pekin Man only knew how to keep up a fire, or if he knew how to produce it.

In the deepest corner of the cave are three skulls of Sinanthropus (the type of Pekin Man); these are family relics surrounded with offerings of various animal skulls and antlers—skulls of Bear, Sabre-toothed Tiger (*Machairodus*), big types of Feline and Wild Boar, Deer (*pseudaxis*) and the antlers of a Megaceros Stag. Several trees of circes (Judas tree), of which there are many seeds in certain levels of the brecchia, are in the left-hand corner of the rock-shelter.

A little distance away and watching the movements of these people, from whom they hope for something eatable, are Hyænas and Wolves ; whilst on the grassy plain beyond the stream Gazelles and other Antelopes graze, and there are Ostriches, Deer of the Megaceros group, Asiatic Wild Asses, an Elephant very like a Mammoth and a Woolly Rhinoceros. A big Feline creeps near to attack the *Spiroceros*. In the air or perching along the sides of the stream are Swallows, Choughs (*Pyrrhocorax*), Vultures, Herons and Ducks.

Away to the left, on the wooded slopes of the far side of the plain, we can distinguish a second cave inhabited by another family of Sinanthropus Man, from which a column of smoke rises.

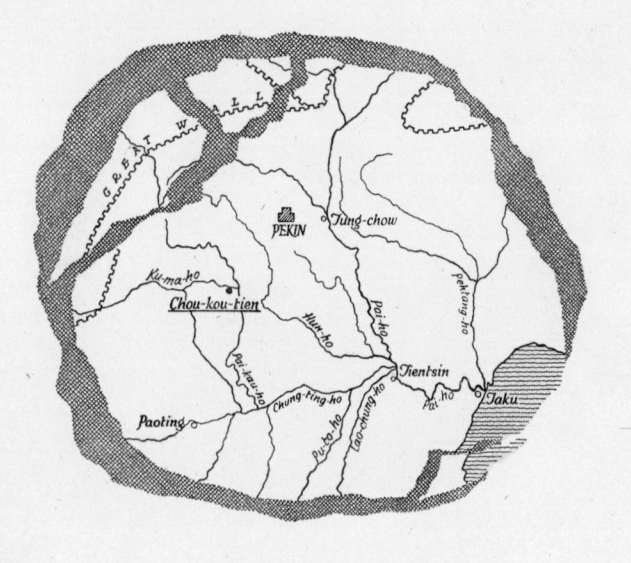

SCENE TWO

Chipping Flint in the Old Palæolithic Days of North-West Europe

PALÆOLITHIC Men, in the age called Abbevillian, certainly knew how to extract flint cores from which they made their tools and weapons. They either dug them out of the chalk itself or at least from the clay containing flint, above the chalk. Here, in some chalky valley in the basin of the Somme or the Thames, you see on the left a Man with a pointed hand-pick busy at this task. The lumps dug out are being collected and placed in piles at some distance by three boys.

The central worker is chopping up one of these blocks with a hammer-stone held in his hand, whilst on the right another Man produces bigger flakes by striking a block on an anvil buried in the soil. Two Women, crouching in the foreground, take their turn in fashioning the large flakes into pointed axes, trimmed on both faces, by striking them on lighter, long anvils held by one

hand ; beside the anvils are the pointed axes and the flakes struck off. Cleavers with a wide cutting edge lie round the outer border of the work-shop.

On the extreme right are several handles shaped like clubs, with an oval hole pierced in the wider part of each. These holes are intended to receive the bases of the pointed axes or cleaver choppers, when finished. One has already been fixed. Behind the boys collecting the flint lumps, a Man is engaged in hafting one of the pointed axes, while his companion executes a war-dance, having completed the hafting of a similar weapon to his satisfaction.

One of the four Women in the background is producing fire by twirling a pivot in a block of wood ; and a fire burns near, roasting a venison ham. Two of the other Women watch the fire-maker, and keep an eye on the children playing close by. Anxious about the unpleasantly near approach of an inquisitive Elephant (*Elephas antiquus*), fortunately separated from her by a ravine, the fourth Woman tries to frighten the huge beast by flourishing a flaming torch.

Exploitation et taille de la Dubois
à Concise, seize sur le Vieux
pour établie des moutons.

Working and Trimmimg Dolerite on the Banks of the Vaal

MANY regions of the globe have no Flint. On the banks of the Vaal, the South Africans of ancient Palæolithic days used Dolerite to make their tools. This they found in the alluvial soil brought by the river. Dolerite is a volcanic rock so extremely hard that it cannot be split into good sized flakes with the hand, even on an anvil, so far more powerful mechanical means had to be employed which shows the remarkable ingenuity of these very ancient Men.

The present writer has ventured to suppose that chipping by blows given by a big block hung on a tripod may have been the method. This block would be swung towards the piece to be split, in the manner of a pendulum—an operation that would need the combined efforts of at least three persons—two to regulate the movement of the swinging rock and to prevent it striking on the return journey, the third to direct and correct the trajectory, whilst being himself protected from the splinters and from the striking block by an ant-heap or a large boulder. This Man would also have to fix the rock from which the flakes were being struck and move it after each blow. Pieces of Dolerite thus obtained would then be handed over to be trimmed on small anvils, so that they could be fashioned into axes by chipping on one or both faces.

Here, in one of the small quarries of pebbles on the Vaal banks, this last process is being carried out by the couple in the right foreground. On the left, two Men are fashioning long flakes into cleavers with blows dealt by a stone held in the hand—" manual percussion "—while their companions behind are hafting the cleavers in wood, bent and fixed by firm splicing. As for the pointed axes, a number was no doubt fixed in handles to serve as a kind of club.

Since the raw material (Dolerite) is found in unlimited quantity on the banks of the Vaal, it is probable that the neighbouring tribes came to obtain their store from there, and in all likelihood brought something in exchange. The immense extent of the river-side work-shops suggests a real commerce, intensively and very intelligently carried on, and—in a way—standardized.

Beyond the Dolerite workers flows the river Vaal in which Hippopotami swim and, on the adjoining slopes, an Elephant, a Rhinoceros and two Lions stalking Kudu antelopes can be seen.

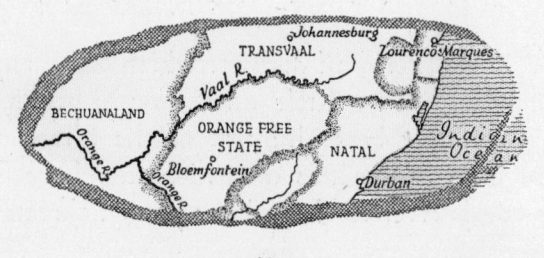

SCENE FOUR

Attacking a She-Bear in her Den

IN a lateral valley in the Périgord district, which has many rock-shelters, is a
cave where a Bear has had her little ones, now grown into fairly big cubs.
Attacking their den are four brave hunters of the Neanderthal race of Men,
armed with wooden lances and clubs on which they have fixed pointed flints.
The great she-bear stands erect to defend her young, threatening the Men with

42

her outstretched paws studded with terrible claws. Women and girls support the hunters, bringing more javelins and encouraging their Menfolk by their cries and gestures.

The shouts of the Men and Women and the vicious growls of the Bears attract a party of helpers from the nearby village which is built on a small plateau and can be reached only by a ladder. Here other spectators follow the fortunes of the fight. Above the Bears' den, Spotted Hyænas and a band of Wolves, brought to the scene of the struggle by the uproar, hope, whatever the outcome, to profit by the corpses after the battle and the remains of the feast which will follow.

Reindeer in the foot of the valley move prudently away, but the grazing Mammoths are not in the least disturbed, nor are the Rhinoceros on the high plateau opposite. Scared by the tumult, two Swans take flight from the river banks and circle overhead.

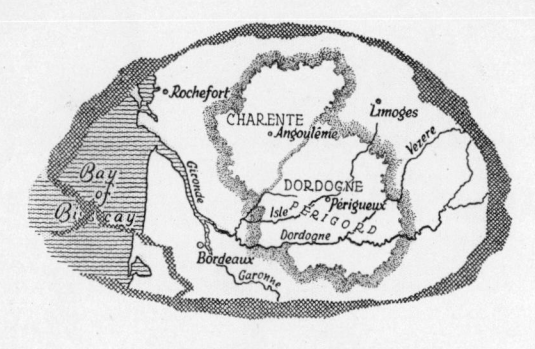

SCENE FIVE

Hunting Bison

SUCH scenes as this took place in Mousterian times and in Upper Palæolithic days. At the mouth of a ravine in a valley encircled by cliffs, in Dordogne or Charente, a herd of Bison is coming down to drink. But hunters armed with javelins are hiding in the hollow stream bed which is bordered with rushes and irises. Four of the Bison are mortally wounded below the shoulder, while a younger one has rolled into the little stream. Behind the hunters Women are bringing extra javelins.

The human types depicted belong more or less to the Upper Palæolithic era; they carry javelins with the barbed bone points bent backwards. The Bison of these times had a real hump of fat lying on the neck behind its head during the warm season, and artists drew it thus in the painted caves. Dried and smoked Bison meat must have fed these hunters many times when the luck of the chase was poor, or climatic changes drove their quarry to seek fresh pastures.

Hunting the Cervus Megaceros

IT is Autumn and the leaves in the forest are golden ; toadstools and certain bushes give a dash of purple and scarlet ; it is the rutting season for the Deer. The big Irish stag—a huge fallow-deer with antlers spreading out into wide palms—is calling for a mate. This is an excellent time to take it by surprise whilst it bells, fights its rivals and pursues the Hinds.

The scene is set in Mousterian times and the Men belong to the race of Neanderthal. Armed with stakes, they are well aware that Panthers are disputing their quarry with them, so most of the Men have hoisted themselves on to the spreading branches of the trees, waiting for the game to pass beneath at arm's length.

At this season numerous toadstools spring up in the forests. Many are edible, such as brown " cêpes "—flap mushrooms—and the girolles, or chanterelle mushrooms, which are orange. Others are dangerous, like the red amanites with white spots which, amongst various tribes in the Arctic zone of north-east Asia, are dried and used in small quantities to produce intoxication.

Mammoth Hunting in Ancient Palæolithic Times in Dordogne

THE action is staged in the narrow valley of the Beune, a tributary of the Vézère, at a short distance from the village of Les Eyzies. Prominent in the background is the celebrated cliff of Font-de-Gaume.

On the narrow plain a party of courageous hunters is attacking a group of Mammoth with lances and axes of the type known as Mousterian with an Acheulean tradition. The enormous creatures try to save themselves by rushing away but several will be hamstrung by axe blows, though not before they have badly injured some of their assailants. Interested spectators are safely perched on the rocky ledges nearby.

On the far side of the water, Woolly Rhinoceros are wandering. With their long curved horns, these are a more dangerous and brutal quarry than their Elephant contemporaries. Man did not risk attacking a Rhinoceros full face, but dug a hole, covered it with branches and hoped that the beast would fall into the trap as one has just done here.

Thousands of years passed before Upper Palæolithic Man used Mammoth ivory to make weapons and statuettes and its grease to light his dwellings and prepare his colours for painting.

Wild Horses Attacked by Lions

HERE is a scene such as the Mousterians and people of the Reindeer Age must often have witnessed. It takes place at a rather wide part of a valley in Périgord. Several Men watch the raid with interest as do the carnivorous Wolves and Bears ; all are hoping to share the prey. On the left, a big Irish stag and

two hinds, on the edge of the plateau, show signs of great alarm. At the foot of the cliffs is a small camp surrounded by a palisade, with a fire to frighten the wild animals.

The wild Horse played a very important part in the food of Fossil Men. At the foot of the hill of Solutré (described in Scene Ten) there was an encampment—probably only in summer—of "Perigordians" (Men of Upper Aurignacian days) who specialized in hunting Horses, filling the whole of a valley with the bones of their victims which have been estimated at more than a hundred thousand.

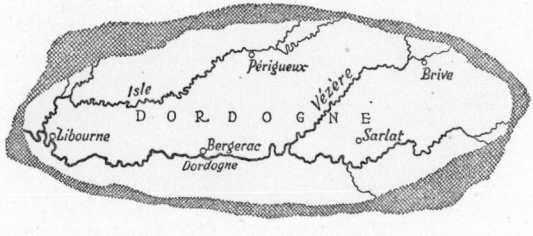

SCENE NINE

Mammoths Visit a Magdalenian Rock-Shelter

IN a countryside similar to that near the Vézère (Dordogne), a Magdalenian family has camped under a rock-shelter and are fishing in the neighbouring stream, whilst their first catch is being cooked or dried for the next meal. The country seems very rich in game, indicating that the camp has only just been established and is, perhaps, but a wayside halt on a journey. Reindeer and Bison graze in the meadow on the far side of the water, and on the higher tablelands Bears, huge Irish Elk with immense antlers and even a Rhinoceros are roaming.

Whilst the people are fishing, three Mammoths, followed at a respectful distance by two Wolves, have approached down the grassy slope. Smelling smoke, they are curious to see what is happening. One looks down suspiciously on the Magdalenians, who display excitement and surprise at the arrival of the great beasts, since the Mammoth had then become rather rare, though a few groups travelled round at the end of this epoch. They must have made a very deep impression on the imagination of Magdalenian Man because, in the cave of Font-de-Gaume, Mammoths are drawn many times in fine lines, cutting across the big polychrome paintings of Bison.

Peering over the rock in the right foreground, a Lioness gazes at the campers inquisitively but her mate is doubtful of the newcomers and wanders away behind the Mammoths.

SCENE TEN

Flint Chipping in Upper Palæolithic Times

EXCEPT for the preliminary roughing out, the technique of working Flint was quite different from that in use in the Old Palæolithic days. The flint core, suitably prepared, was fixed against something firm and long narrow flakes were struck off with the help of a driver. This tool—used to tap in the manner of a chisel—is being employed by the Woman in the left foreground. The blades, struck off the core, are falling into a sort of skin basket. Although these flakes can be used without further working for cutting, or as lance points, they are nearly always trimmed by secondary chipping to serve special purposes such as scrapers, awls, burins or wedges.

The group of flint chippers which you see here, is engaged in fashioning those splendid tools—called Solutrean (from Solutré in Saône-et-Loire)—cut into shapes like laurel or willow leaves. The Woman who is reclining as she works is striking a piece of flint, fixed in a groove in a wooden anvil-block, with a round wooden club. The first part of the work consists in striking off wide thin flakes crosswise, during which the flint very often breaks. The second stage is directed to making the edges of the flint even ; these edges have to be made thinner by very fine regular chipping with a pressure flaking tool of stone, bone or hard wood. This is what the Woman in the centre is doing. Four points which she has finished are lying in front of her.

Behind the anvil-block an elderly Woman has fixed a laurel-leaf point on the split end of a wooden handle and is fastening it more firmly with vegetable or animal fibre. The three Men in the background are already equipped with similar lances; one is throwing his like a javelin; another, who has a bow, is using his—which have far smaller points—as arrows. It is not certain whether the bow was used in France at this time but it was definitely in use in Eastern Spain.

The racial types shown belong to the higher forms of *Homo sapiens*, having come from the East and South-East outside Europe and destroyed and taken the place of the Neanderthal race which was far more primitive. Suggested in the landscape are the limestone cliffs near Solutré, in the neighbourhood of Macon. At the foot of one of these cliffs the celebrated site of Cro-du-Charnier was found, where the Upper Palæolithic peoples continued to live from Aurignacian to Solutrean days and into the Old Magdalenian times.

I have not clothed my Men and Women because, except in the cold season, they probably wore no clothes; and also because any attempt to depict fashions of which we know nothing seems to me to be too imaginative.

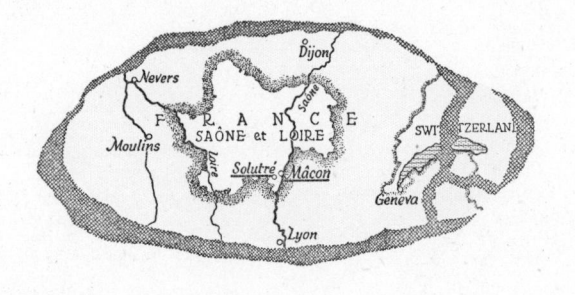

SCENE ELEVEN

Working Bone and Deerhorn in Magdalenian Times

IN ancient and Middle Palæolithic times, especially in those districts where Flint was rare, Bone was used as a form of "animal stone" and cut by flaking. Deerhorn, also, was employed as an "animal wood," being cut and broken like tree branches. But it was not until Upper Palæolithic times that an industry in Bone, Deerhorn (mostly Reindeer antler) and Ivory was extensively developed. At that period these raw materials were cut into shape with a Burin. This was a tool with a narrow vertical bevel on the end of an oblong flake or blade, and with

it parallel grooves, deep enough to reach the spongy tissue, were cut. In this way a long rod was defined which was later detached by cutting it free beneath. If the antler was too big in the first place, it was chopped into pieces by the sharp angle that is seen at the base of certain flint cores which were the only heavy stone tools used by the people of Upper Palæolithic times.

This scene is set in another corner of the valley of the Vézère (Dordogne) or in that neighbourhood. The Man standing on the left is cutting a large antler in the manner described above, whilst his two neighbours squatting nearby are using the Burin. Curved or straight rods which they have already cut lie around them on the ground. Here, also, lies the shin bone of a Horse from which the right-hand craftsman has cut very fine slips. After polishing on a grooved sandstone slab, these will be made into eyed needles.

The seated young girl in the central group is polishing small rods on a grooved pebble. The other is piercing the eye of a needle with a very sharp flint borer, while the standing Woman is scraping a short rod in a notched flint blade to make it round. On the ground at her feet are spindle-shaped javelins and some wider pieces from which the workman kneeling near is cutting harpoon barbs, having first drawn their shape with a sharp point. At his back, a Woman is hafting the points of harpoons, both in pairs and singly.

Two of the finished harpoons have already been seized by a lad who is setting off with them to the river from which his friend is returning with the results of his fishing. Under the shadow of the cliffs a seamstress is sewing or mending fur garments for autumn hunting expeditions.

SCENE TWELVE

The Preparation of Skins

IN a rock-shelter on a ledge high above the river embankment, the Magdalenians are busy preparing skins from which they intend to make clothing for the bad season. After cutting open its stomach with a sharp flint, the Woman in the foreground is skinning a young fawn which the hunters have killed. The Man standing near her has hung up and fixed a fresh skin to the branch of a tree ; armed with a side-scraper, he is cleaning off the fat and flesh clinging to the inner surface. On the right, another fresh skin is being stretched flat on the ground and fixed with wooden pegs driven in all round the edges so that it does not shrink whilst drying.

At the nearby fire an old couple warm themselves ; the Man is, perhaps, blind and his wife is describing to him what she sees. Away beyond them under the rock-shelter, a band of children is playing. Moving along a ledge of the

cliff opposite is a Bear which is probably trying to approach the Stag and two Hinds grazing on the neighbouring plateau.

SCENE THIRTEEN

A Natural Circus in Upper Palæolithic (Magdalenian) Days

PERFORMANCES such as this must often have taken place at the end of the Palæolithic age. Here, in a hollow valley in the limestone country of Lot, two Panthers are trying to attack a herd of wild Horses on its way to its watering place. Most of the herd takes flight, but the Stallion, furious, fights back successfully, crushing the Panthers with its front hoofs and savaging them with its strong teeth. In Spain, I once saw a Stallion thus pursuing an enormous dog which only saved its life by headlong flight.

The noise of this fierce combat has attracted the attention of numerous onlookers and a tribe of Men living in the neighbouring rock-shelters are watching the scene with pleasure. The Men are exchanging opinions on the chances of the fight; one of the elders, happy to see his grandchildren playing at his feet under the close care of their mothers, makes the Women laugh by his witty remarks. Two hunters armed with javelins with bone barbs are, perhaps, waiting for the end of the drama to dispute the victims with the Wolves. One of the Women is maybe wondering if she will gain a fine fur as the result of the Stallion's struggle with the Panther.

In the holes of the rock above, the Squirrel and the Ravens are apparently quite unconcerned. But down below two grey Mountain Hares, which change their coats according to the season, are getting out of the way with rapidity. Storks and Ducks are uncertain about it all, and the Swans are out of harm's way already. The two Wolves at the foot of the cliff wait for the end, convinced that they will gain something whatever the outcome of the fight. In the distance, Bears and Lions exhibit only vague interest.

SCENE FOURTEEN

Salmon Running

THE running upstream of the Salmon was certainly, in the Reindeer Age, one of the definite food resources of the tribes at the beginning of the fine season, as it still is for many Indian, Eskimo, Tungus and Chukchi peoples in America and in Arctic Asia. All the wild flesh-eating animals in those countries also profit by this harvest as much as they can. On certain days the rivers contain literally more fish than water and each hungry beast can help itself as long as

strength and appetite permit.

So it is that in this scene in some shallow rapids of the Vézère, near the classic rock-shelters of La Madeleine (Dordogne), we see on the far bank of the river Wolves, Bears and Hyænas and wading Birds catching the smaller Fish for themselves while the fishing Eagles seize everything they can.

The Magdalenian fishermen, armed with harpoons, some in the water and others on the near bank, make the most of this magnificent but brief chance of securing a store of food. It is chiefly the Men's affair to catch the big Fish, but the Women are just as busy, some piling the Salmon caught by their Men in heaps, others cleaning them. Others again hang the Fish on strings above a

small fire to dry and smoke them, although some will be eaten immediately. In the foreground, several hunters are watching over the safety of the fishermen and building fires to scare the Wolves should they become too bold.

SCENE FIFTEEN

Passage of the Reindeer in the Autumn

IT is late autumn—time of the annual migration of the Reindeer. On the undulating tablelands and rounded granite hill-tops of Limousin the first snow covers the ground. Coming from the borders of the Scandinavian or German glaciers where they have passed the summer, the herds travel south with instinctive precision, always by the same roads ; and, as on previous occasions, the Magdalenian Men have arranged an ambush. Fires flame along the nearby hills to prevent the Reindeer from turning aside from their centuries-old path in the course of which the hunters have planned their stalking place. Crouched behind a horseshoe of sunken boulders they hope that they will only be seen by their quarry at the last moment.

Escorted by several old males, a herd of Reindeer has just crossed a neighbouring pass and is coming down the nearside slope. The boulders entrap the beasts within the semi-circle of hunters, who spring up and attack them with their javelins whilst waiting their chance to kill them with short clubs. These weapons are similar to those used today by the Indians in Athabaska on the edges of the forests and the great Arctic plains.

I have dressed my hunters in the Eskimo manner, with tunics of reindeer skin, trousers of bear skin and fur-lined leather boots. The life of the tribe must certainly have depended on this hunting in early winter, especially if the summer hunting had not provided them with a sufficient quantity of smoked and dried meat.

SCENE SIXTEEN

Big Game Hunting Which Brought Forth Great Art

COURAGE and daring were not virtues in those far-off times but essential qualities if life were to be preserved ; without them came death from hunger, save to the shell-fish eaters. Men lived dangerously then, and it was from incidents such as this that they developed the gift of drawing animals in rapid action. With a wealth of such encounters in his memory, fossil Man came to produce extraordinarily vivid pictures of this kind which, as his tech-

nique improved, became masterly in the decoration of caves and small objects.

The action depicted here takes place on the meadow-covered slopes of the lower Pyrenean hills. Pursued by beaters, four Bison rush blindly into an ambuscade where hunters have lain hidden behind rocks. The encounter is violent. One of the Bison, struck in the hollow below its shoulder by a hunter's lance, falls to its knees only after wounding its assailant who rolls on the ground clutching the broken end of the spear shaft. Meantime, another hunter prepares to deal the Bison a blow on the head with a club that has a sharp, pointed stone fixed in it.

A second Bison in its mad career attempts to break through the attackers, two of whom get ready to strike. Slightly behind, the third animal bellows with fear, turning its head as it tries to stop. Still farther in the rear, the last Bison watches the slaughter without checking its flight.

In prehistoric times in Europe, Bison are almost always shown with a lump between the back of the neck and the hump, which Bison today do not possess. This would certainly seem to be of fat, like the camel's hump, and the animals must have developed it during the summer and it must have melted in the winter.

[This drawing is reproduced by kind permission of Mrs. Diana Dent.]

SCENE SEVENTEEN

Alpine Sports in the Reindeer Age

IN the summer season, Men of Upper Palæolithic times climbed the mountain sides to hunt Bears which roamed there eating bilberries. Ibex or Chamois, feeding on the high-perched meadows, were other quarry. Marmots, too, were prized for their edible flesh and for their skins which could be sewn together to make supple garments. Certain small caves in the Vercors district (Dauphiné) were full of the bones of these animals, no doubt trapped by Man in the summer months.

Here, while a Bear is being attacked by men with lances, two archers are stalking a troop of Alpine Ibex. They are having an arduous time scaling the steep rocks at the far side of a belt of pine, fir and spruce. Overhead, an Eagle watches the activities of these hardy hunters.

At the foot of a deep ravine flows a glacier which has much shrunk already, although it is still meagrely fed from the now-melting snowfields (*névé*). Big, erratic boulders from a far older lateral moraine lie scattered over a bank where grow Rhododendrons and other Alpine flowers, such as Gentians, Martagon Lilies, Narcissi and furry Anemones.

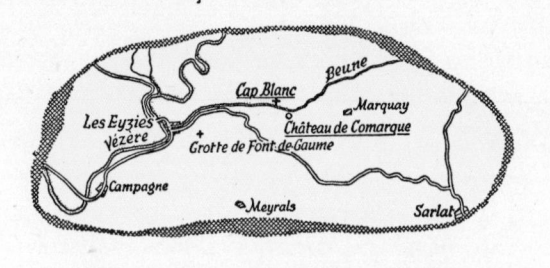

SCENE EIGHTEEN

Sculptors at Work in the Rock-Shelter of Cap Blanc

THIS is the valley of the Beune, not far from Les Eyzies (Dordogne), where it joins the Vézère. The cliffs here, not being so high, have deeper shelters, thus providing better living conditions in summer during the hunting season. In the Middle Ages a castle with a fortified keep was built at Comarque across the narrow valley. When it fell into ruin, the charming castle of Laussel arose, which combined a country house with a defensive position against lightly armed marauding bands. Near at hand is the sculptured rock-shelter of Cap Blanc of which this drawing gives a free interpretation.

This rock-shelter was decorated at an early period in Magdalenian days with splendid high reliefs, akin to those on separate slabs dating from the end of Solutrean times in the valley du Roc, near Sers (Charente). From these two sources I have drawn the inspiration for the figures on the rock wall here. The two white-haired sculptors are regarding their handiwork with satisfaction. Some of the heavy flint tools employed to engrave and scrape the limestone, sometimes to a depth of more than eight inches, lie around them. Chips and dust from the rock cover the ground with a yellowish carpet beneath which grey ashes left by other camps appear here and there. Two hunters, armed with javelins and hooked throwing-sticks—used to increase the range of the javelins—are clearly interested in the half-magical half-artistic work of the professional sculptors, who are also probably sorcerers. The reliefs themselves portray a Stallion trotting round a Mare, just as is happening in one of the

neighbouring fields, and a Bison in very fine condition, as it would be at the end of summer.

In the right foreground two pupils are preparing the colours—one the red, the other the black—which will be used to colour the sculptures. They pound the rocky pieces of ochre, collected on the nearby tablelands, in mortars. Next, they will crush the coarse sand obtained by the first operation into fine powder on the mill-stone beyond them. Eventually the coloured powders will be put into shells and a cup made from the top of a skull. On the big palette

Sculptors at Work in the Rock-Shelter of Cap Blanc

where the colour will be kneaded with grease, a supple bone spatula with an ornamented handle is waiting, between the ochre and the grease. When all is ready and the season more advanced, magical ceremonies will take place here, as in the dark caverns.

On the marshy floor of the valley, above which Duck are flying, Horses and Wild Cattle graze, watched by Wolves on the edge of the thick woods at the foot of the cliffs. Two Lions are warming themselves in the sun on the opposite cliff tops.

SCENE NINETEEN

Magdalenian Funeral Ceremony

BELOW the sculptured frieze in the rock-shelter of Cap Blanc near Les Eyzies (Dordogne) was a sepulchre of some probably important person who was lying in a cramped attitude, suggesting that, like his contemporary at Raymonden (Chancelade), he had been bound together so as to occupy the least possible space. Though this position is not shown here, I give that found elsewhere in other burials in Upper Palæolithic times, as at Grimaldi and Solutré, where the body lies stretched out on the ground. For the setting of this funeral ceremony, I have chosen Cap Blanc, or a similar site in the same valley.

The dead man—a Chief—has been laid upon a bed of powdered ochre, brought in a basket. He is adorned with his necklace and diadem of coloured beads. On his chest lies a pierced baton of reindeer horn (an arrow-straightener ?), and a dagger with a long flint blade ; awls and punches are arranged near his right shoulder, and a wolf skin is partly drawn across his body.

A young Woman, his daughter or his favourite wife, stoops tenderly over his face, talking to him as if he could hear. Other Women carry stones with which to surround and cover the body and preserve it from the attacks of wild beasts.

With grief-stricken faces, two near relations or friends, wearing their ceremonial hoods fashioned from the heads of Panther and Lynx, preside over these preparations for the burial. The young Men standing at the entrance of the shelter are being harangued by the new Chief, who is recalling the virtues, courageous acts and audacity of the dead man. They listen with deep attention. On the walls of the rock-shelter are bas-reliefs rubbed with ochre, and at the feet of the corpse lies the head of a freshly-killed Reindeer—provision for the long journey.

SCENE TWENTY

Wild Cattle Crossing a Wide River

IN the valley of the Dordogne, where there is a broad plain bordered by cliffs and steep slopes, the time has come for the Wild Cattle to leave for lands where the winter is less severe. It is autumn, and they will return next spring.

There were big herds of such Cattle in ancient Mousterian and Upper Aurignacian days. They were of two kinds—one very big, and the other smaller with a long head. All present-day domestic breeds of Cattle are produced from a mixture of these two, except the humped kind (Zebu). Since these

wild animals used their horns for fighting, these were naturally well developed, being set high, slanting well forward and growing in the shape of a lyre.

The Cattle swim splendidly—their bodies are completely submerged. (I have observed a scene similar to this in the province of Cadiz, when the river Barbate was in flood.) A group of Ducks or Geese, frightened by the splashing in the water, seeks a quieter refuge ; while a human spectator, climbing a tree for safety, has infuriated one of the bulls. On the opposite bank, hunters armed with lances run to kill some of the Cattle as they land.

SCENE TWENTY-ONE

A Model Poses for an Aurignacian Sculptor

AT this time, the art of engraving and drawing on rock-shelters and caves was already fully developed. But it was chiefly on small objects that the human figure was represented ; at first most of these took the form of female figures sculptured in the round on ivory and also on detached slabs of rock. An Aurignacian sculptor is here seen at work on one of these ivory figurines in a rock-shelter in a Périgord valley. Around him are his materials and tools, and other examples of his art.

Hands outlined in colour, sometimes with fingers missing—cut off—also date from the dawn of this age. Those drawn on cave walls were by no means coarse or clumsy as might have been supposed in this early race. Although occasionally mutilated, they are the hands of artists. Animal figures, also drawn in outline, soon followed.

Lances of this period were armed with flat bone points, some of which had

a split base to be inserted at the tip of the javelin shaft. The Mammoth and Woolly Rhinoceros abounded in those days, and the Lion and Cave Bear were frequently met with.

SCENE TWENTY-TWO

Trading with Ornamental Shells

SHELLS, both of the kinds which exist today and those that are now fossil, were much appreciated in Upper Palæolithic times and were the basis of a brisk two-way commerce between the Atlantic and the Mediterranean. Fossil shells were found near Bordeaux, at Grignon (Seine et Oise), at Cuise (Oise), and in Belgium and in Moravia, which must have been traded very far from their place of origin, as well as our modern shells.

Here we suppose this trade to be in the hands of a nomad Mediterranean population carrying their stock of shells from place to place across western Europe and exchanging them for furs and flint tools of better quality and workmanship than those of their own region. I have set this scene in the Tardoire valley of the Charente, not very far from the present town of La Rochefoucauld. The cave with a portico-like entrance is inspired by that of Le Placard, at Rochebertier. Other shelters are quite near, cut in the limestone hillock of Bois-du-Rocher at Vilhonneur which is seen in the left background.

The six Men and Women on the left are of southern race, as is the old negroid slave in the centre of the right-hand group who belong to the local population. The Women from Le Placard, very excited at the sight of the beautiful, coloured shell necklaces, try to persuade their husbands to humour their longing to adorn themselves. But the Men are striving to restrain their Womenfolk, one of them being extremely loth even to leave the shelter, although urged to do so by the insistent shouts of his spouse.

Holding the hand of this disappointed wife is a tiny child, who shows far more interest in the flight of a butterfly. Between the old man who is attempting to turn a deaf ear to the entreaties of his very young wife, or daughter, and the persuasive negroid, another child is much intrigued since he has never seen such big cowries as are offered, although there are red shells sewn on the short skirt that he wears. This decorated garment is similar to those worn by two children buried in one of the Grimaldi caves at Mentone. Greatly impressed by the beauty of the young Mediterranean woman who holds the centre of the scene, a handsome lad of Cro-Magnon type listens amiably to what she says while exchanging a number of finely worked blades of excellent flint for a few big Cypreas.

On the rock serving as a counter are a big Pecten shell, more cowries, some Murex, with Turritellas and Ceriths. Business seems to be in full swing with the nomad visitors.

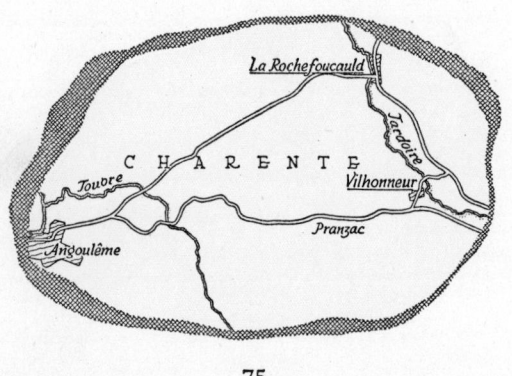

Hunting Disguises and Drawing from Life in Magdalenian Times

BISON, Reindeer and wild Horses graze on a plateau against a background of rounded hills where Marmots have their burrows, as can be seen from the earth mounds which they have thrown up. On the left, a hunter disguised in a wolf skin—in much the same way as certain Red Indians camouflaged themselves for a similar purpose at the beginning of the last century—crawls towards one of the Bison. Excited and attracted by the strange "Wolf," the beast approaches him, followed by several others. A second hunter, covered with the skin of a young Reindeer complete with antlers, is enticing two of the Reindeer, who venture near, full of curiosity.

But a third Reindeer has halted, for it has scented the Man hidden behind a few bushes growing amongst an outcrop of rock, who is sketching one of the Reindeer. Although it is certain that the big paintings and huge frescoes in the dark caverns were drawn from memory, it is reasonable to conclude that the artists trained themselves by sketching from Nature. Drawing with a flint point would be made on flat stone—a kind of notebook or sketching block of which hundreds are sometimes found in the Magdalenian levels.

SCENE TWENTY-FOUR

Grinding Ochre and Painting Frescoes on Rock

THE use of mineral colouring material, such as Ochre, is general; even before the Reindeer Age we find many pieces used in the Neanderthal sites. All shades, ranging from bright yellow to vermilion red and sepia brown, are provided by the ochreous clays, in which fragments of more or less rock-like ochre are found on the tablelands of Périgord and many other parts. The people certainly used them to paint their bodies, although I have not illustrated this, as being too imaginative. Caves and frescoed rock-shelters in south-west France and Spain, to mention Europe only, contain hundreds of paintings made with these colours.

In this scene, an artist of that time assisted by a pupil is finishing the painting of a Reindeer, executed on a rock wall. Meanwhile, three Women prepare the colours. One pounds pieces of ochre in a mortar; another rubs the coarse powder obtained from this first operation so as to make it finer; while the third uses a flexible bone spatula to mix the powder with grease. A shell, a kind of Pecten, serves as a temporary container for the colour, and the shoulder-blade of an Ox for a palette on which to try out the shades obtained.

In France or north-west Spain, paintings of this kind are only preserved if they are in dark passages; but in eastern Spain, many painted rock-shelters are in full daylight. Sometimes in Périgord, a fall of rock from the roof and sides has permitted paintings which were not destroyed to be preserved in the soil.

The Sanctuary of Trois Frères at Montesquieu-Avantès (Ariège)

MEN of the Reindeer Age ventured deep into the dark galleries of the underground caves. Traces of them are found 1,850 yards from the entrance, as at Niaux, and on the far side of what are often dangerous crossings. They did not, apparently, live there for long since the only remains of food refuse are near the entrance, but they walked about the galleries freely by the light of torches, or more often lamps—a flat piece of rock with a lump of grease and a wick. These they must undoubtedly have been able to relight in a few moments, thanks to some sort of fire-drill.

Judging by the deer antlers, either shed or not, of which there is an accumulation at the cave entrances in the south-west of France, the people lived there only from November to February. Perhaps the even temperature of from 52 to 57 degrees Fahrenheit in the dark galleries of the majority of the caves seemed very pleasant to them during the days of severe winter cold when, at the same time, the frost outside stopped all infiltration of water. It was almost certainly in winter, therefore, when the intense frost and thick snow made hunting difficult or completely impossible, that the caves were most inhabited. Conditions were, in fact, similar to those now obtaining with the Eskimos.

This is the season when the latter hold their tribal reunions to initiate the young people in their new obligations as adults and instruct them in the traditions of the tribe. On such occasions magico-religious ceremonies are also performed, including masked dances and invocations to celestial beings or spirits designed to ensure the multiplication of game, the destruction of wild beasts and good fortune in forthcoming hunting expeditions during the summer.

The communicating underground system of deep corridors cut out in the limestone by the Volp at Montesquieu-Avantès, (today divided into two separate caverns and called the Tuc d'Audoubert and the Trois Frères), which end to end must stretch for 1,550 yards, certainly witnessed such ceremonies for many thousands of years. This scene attempts to show one such taking place in the apse, the walls of which are covered with hundreds of incised drawings presided over by the single figure of a horned Man drawn in black at a spot which appears inaccessible. The hall is on a lower level than the general plan of the corridors and the entrance is down a rather steep and slippery slope of stalagmite. A narrow passage, adorned with springing arches and arcades of stalagtite, leads beyond. This I have shown lit by invisible fires, with young people moving about on the red clay soil and silhouetted in the window-like openings like figures in a shadow play. The " Sanctuary " is seen here from the middle of its right-hand wall. Seated on the steps of the stalagmitic slope mentioned above are the young initiates behind whom stand three of their teachers wearing ceremonial costume heads of Bear and Reindeer. Each carries a harpoon and a lamp with grease sufficient to guide them but not to illuminate the hall. This is done by the two fires rather lower down, the light from which strikes upwards. A man has been detailed to keep these fires going by throwing small branches on them from time to time.

The far wall of the apse is covered with incised figures of Horses, Bison, Ibex and Reindeer; I have drawn there one of the Lion heads placed in the passage some hundred yards nearer the entrance, and which seems to threaten imprudent violators of the mysteries. I have placed against this wall, also, the two Bison modelled in clay in the cave of Tuc d'Audoubert which is now separated from the Trois Frères cave. Each of these leans against a block of limestone; together, they represent a Bull following a Cow, symbolic of a magical rite of reproduction. To their right, I have brought from the Pyrenean cave at Montespan, near St. Gaudens (Haute Garonne), the headless clay Bear, and set it in front of an engraving which is actually in this cave of Trois Frères and which depicts exactly the same subject. The clay model of the Bear at Montespan, pierced by many javelins, was also covered with a fresh bear-skin (as I have shown it), the true head being fixed to the clay model and held there by a pole stuck in it. The tufts of grass stained red are a restoration of the neighbouring engraving.

Of the four actors, three of whom caper about, the one on the right—the Man-Bison—is a precise copy of an

80

engraving in the nearby corridor. He probably represents a mythical ancestor—a kind of Orpheus, playing a musical bow. On the wall at his back, he has for company animals whose characteristics have been wilfully mixed—a Reindeer with the fore-feet of a Duck, a Hind with the fore-quarters of a Bison. Two of the other three performers are only variants of the first. The Bison skins which they wear are obviously not the real thing, for these would be far too big and heavy; they are copies on a small scale. It is these two actors who at lengthy intervals stick a stake into the clay body of the Bear near them. The fourth actor, dressed in a Bear skin, recalls a similar figure—though in that instance he is dancing—on a thin bone disc coming from Mas d'Azil.

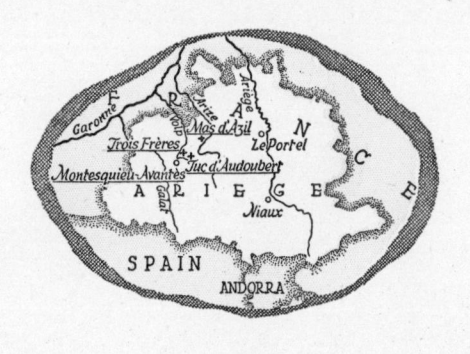

Above the musician and out of arm's reach is a figure of the "God," painted in black and engraved. His antlers, which in the cave are only engraved, are those of a big Irish Elk, not of a Reindeer or a Red Deer. His round owlish eyes indicate that he must see in the night; there is no mouth beneath his nose, only a long beard to signify that he is an "Eternal Father." His arms are flexed and the half-open hands stretch forward as if to seize something. He seems to be dancing and has a rather bushy tail like that of a Wolf, an animal which steals around without noise. The sex is undoubtedly masculine. We have wrongly named him the "Sorcerer," but like Cernunnos of the Gauls who thousands of years later resembled him, the "God," as the Reindeer hunters imagined him, presided here—as in Nature—over all animals. Like the deity of certain Eskimos, he assured their increase. This scene is, in fact, a sort of Rogation procession such as we celebrate still at the beginning of summer to call down on the harvest the blessing of the true Christian God.

The position of the drawing of the "God" is not so inaccessible as it appears. With a little gymnastic effort it is possible to come face to face with him by climbing out of the window in the rock to his right and using a projecting point on which to place your foot and turn towards him. This window is easily reached by going through one or other of the openings below. These lead through narrow passages, covered with admirable drawings, to a short steep upward slope which brings you by narrow channels, where there are a few drawings, to the keystone of the vault of this hall. Engravings in these passages make it clear that the actors in these ceremonies passed that way, perhaps shouting or singing in such a fashion that the initiates would think the cries supernatural. Invisible to the audience below, one of these oracles is concealed behind the engraving of the sorcerer and, as Chief Sorcerer, may have consulted with his assistant who is hidden in a corner where there are also a great number of engravings.

SCENE TWENTY-SIX

Palæolithic Rock Painters of Eastern Spain

SOME of the tribes of Reindeer and Bison hunters went south, following the Mediterranean seaboard into Catalonia, and along the coastal districts as far as Almeria. The climate here was milder and although Rhinoceros, Bison and Elk ventured into these parts only occasionally, a rich fauna of wild Cattle and Horses, Ibex, wild Boar, Red Deer and sometimes Fallow-deer made the region very desirable. So the newcomers settled in all the valleys leading down from the mountain slopes of the high rocky plateau of Castile.

In the daylit rock-shelters they painted many frescoes, smaller than those of their cousins who had remained north of the Pyrenees. Apart from the reduced size, their animal figures exactly resembled the more archaic work of the northerners; but whilst in Franco-Cantabrian art human figures are very rarely attempted, either assembled in scenes together or with animals, the painted panels of eastern Spain show many hunting and sometimes war scenes or other aspects of tribal life.

We are, therefore, better informed as regards the weapons, clothing and ornaments of these peoples here than anywhere else in prehistoric times. They had the bow and feathered arrows, wore feathers in their hair and ornaments on their legs and arms. Most of the activities shown here are directly inspired by these pictures, including the Man climbing up a rope ladder to a hive of wild Bees, and the wild Boar hunt. Baskets are also painted on the rocks, but that they were used for drawing or carrying water is purely my suggestion. The Women in frocks and the one leading a child by the hand, as well as the Chief with his feather head-dress, are copied exactly from the painted rock panels. The setting of this scene is inspired partly by Maestrazygo (Castellón) and partly by Alpera (Albacete).

SCENE TWENTY-SEVEN

The Shell-Fish Eaters of the Sea-Shore

IN every age, the tribes living on the shores of all countries have gathered the shell-fish to be found on the reefs exposed at low tide, and have also been fishermen of some kind or another. This scene attempts to show what life was like along the western coast of Portugal. The background of the landscape is inspired by the outline of the Sierra de Sintra, near the coast at Cabo

da Roca, whence the foaming ocean breakers are seen—a site not very far from Guincho.

This coast is riddled with shelters hollowed out by the waves of an earlier sea and in them live several families of the Upper Palæolithic or Mesolithic age. At the edge of the ebbing tide the children cast their fishing lines, weighted by notched pebbles which are found in quantities at certain sites on the shore of the Minho. They are hauling in fine big fish. Others, with the Women,

collect shell-fish clinging to the rocks and hunt Crabs which are hiding until the tide comes in. The shell-fish are hacked from the rocks with a pebble roughly worked into a thick or a bevelled point. Thousands of these are found on the ancient sea-beaches of this coast, in the beaches of the last interglacial period and even amongst the rocks only exposed at the season of the equinoctial tides. When, in post-glacial times, these people were deprived of some of their shell-fish-bearing rocks by a rise in the sea level, they were forced to emigrate to the Cantabrian coast in Asturias where the tools were first discovered and therefore called Asturian.

The Men were rather indifferent hunters of small Game, Rabbits and Ducks ; I have imagined that they had bows, since these were in general use in the east of the Peninsula and are seen in the Upper Palæolithic Mediterranean frescoes there.

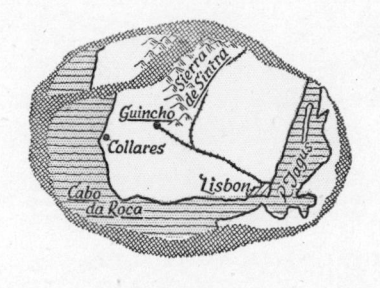

SCENE TWENTY-EIGHT

The Azilians at Mas d'Azil

THE setting of this scene is at the southern entrance, up-stream, of the vast cavern of Mas d'Azil. Through this great natural tunnel the Arize flows, piercing the limestone range of Plantaurel. Here the largest sites of the Azilian civilization, going back as far as the Mesolithic period, were discovered by Edouard Piette. The climate had become damp and temperate; Red and Roe Deer, Elk and wild Boar had replaced the Reindeer which had emigrated. Fishing, gathering snails and hunting mammals were the chief sources of food supply. An entire tribe of Azilians lived under the wide vault of the southern hall which was almost lit by daylight.

You see them here busy with their daily occupations. On the right, the old Chief tries to keep his ancient limbs warm with fur garments arranged in squares of varied colours; he is watching the children playing, for his family is numerous. A pretty young Woman brings him a dish of snails with the bone stiletto to pick them out of their shells; a few empty shells lie on the ground at his feet. Both the Chief and his attendant wear crowns of shells. At the old man's side and under his personal guard are five big pebbles painted with diagrammatic

signs, perhaps " churingas," in which the souls of the tribe's ancestors live. The Chief's Dog looks with pride at his master—it is something to belong to a Chief !

Near at hand, one of the Chief's sons is fishing. Armed with a harpoon with a flat point and a double row of barbs, he is trying to catch the large fish in the river, with some success. Behind him, another young Woman carries faggots on her shoulder to help in the cooking of one of the fish which has already been threaded on a spit and is being closely watched by a kneeling Man and a Dog stretched out in the warmth.

On the left, a hunter leaning on a harpoon is consulting two Women on the likelihood of success in a future hunting expedition; they are no doubt clairvoyant and in place of cards are using pebbles painted with divers signs such as bars and spots. Near them lie trophies of the hunt—skulls of Deer, Bison and Ibex—and a red Dog gnaws a bone; it is in this Age that the Dog is first found in the company of Man.

On the roof of the domed hut a little farther away are the skulls of a Red Deer and an Elk. These animals were fairly abundant in the Pyrenees at that time. In front of the door of the hut a Man sits warming himself on the hearth of a fire which his wife is poking. On a flat stone at his side are some snails, and there are more cooking. A Roe Deer which he has killed in a recent hunt is nearby. The neighbouring hut, topped with the skulls of Bison and Bear, backs against a shallow bank. From it a Woman has just come out to pat a Dog returning from the chase; a second Dog is jumping down the bank, while a third looks eagerly at a wild Boar which is being carried in by the two hunters armed with bows who have slain it.

On the far bank of the river, close to a Woman with a fishing-rod, children are romping amongst a great mass of fallen rocks. At the foot of the rock wall, framed by an arch and column of stalagmite, a painter is executing diagrams similar to those seen in the cave of Marsoulas in a valley of the Salat, where they are painted on top of the naturalistic frescoes of the Reindeer Age. The artist has already completed a Man and a Woman in geometric style, a four-footed animal and a right hand, reduced to a few lines for the outspread fingers and a bent thumb. Towards the entrance of the cavern are two domed huts, the inhabitants of which are warming themselves at the fire or cooking. Trophy skulls are fixed on the tops of long poles driven into the ground beside the huts.

Through the wide opening, we see the forest covering the slopes upstream from the cave. On the higher, rocky crests a Bear chases a herd of Deer; even a Lion is there. This is the last epoch in which this big feline survived in France. Swifts nesting in the clefts of the towering roof of the cavern fly round in rapid circles.

SCENE TWENTY-NINE

Red Deer Hunting in Mesolithic Days

THE Red Deer found in so many parts of the Mediterranean and Iberian regions was hailed as a herald of summer in the countries where the Reindeer came in winter. It did not move towards warmer lands until the end of autumn. The state of the antlers of the animals in this scene shows that the summer is far advanced—a season when the Stags are still herding together and the Hinds keeping in separate herds, although they have two of their younger fawns with them.

Bows and arrows were certainly in general use at this time from the Pyrenees to the Straits of Gibraltar, at least in the Mediterranean province. Such a scene as this might be placed in the Mesolithic Age, or even later.

SCENE THIRTY

Hunting the Elk in South Scandinavia in the Mesolithic Epoch

IN the Mesolithic epoch, at what is known in Scandinavia as the Maglemosian stage, when the last big glacier of the Baltic had withdrawn towards the Scandinavian mountains about ten thousand years ago, the pine forests spread once more over the country and the climate became mild and damp. Tribes of hunters, related to those Magdalenian ones who hunted the Reindeer in France, followed the Deer—and even more eagerly the Elks, which were then greatly increasing in number—into their forests.

Wild Boars, Beavers and Otters lived in the marshes and on the river banks. The tribes themselves dwelt in huts built on a foundation of piles in the flooded

marshes, the piles being supported by an accumulation of bundles of faggots which formed a sort of springy mattress.

The Elk is the biggest but also the least graceful of all the Deer. Various varieties of Elk still exist, one in Scandinavia and another in Canada (Moose).

SCENE THIRTY-ONE

Mesolithic Settlements near the Mouth of the Tagus

WHEN the temperature reached its highest point after the retreat of the glaciers, the sea level rose very slightly but enough for the waters of the great estuary of the Tagus, which is over fifty miles in length, to encourage the breeding of ocean and salt-water fish and shell-fish. The Mesolithic population, who used the tiny triangular or trapeze-shaped tools to barb their arrows, settled in villages on the islands and in the loops of the Tagus tributaries on the left bank of the river, near the point where nowadays stands the little town of Muge (at one time called Mugem). Today this region suffers greatly from malaria (paludism).

Heaps of shells, the remains of the meals of these people, form huge mounds on the banks of these streams. The mounds also contain the bones of Rabbit, Deer, wild Oxen and Horses, wild Boar, Wolf, Fox, Brown Bear, Lynx, Beaver, a few Seal, and many Birds. The bone and deer-horn in these heaps are roughly worked and some shells have been used as personal ornaments. For the first time we find a very few domesticated Dogs. There is no pottery. We can be certain that these people had canoes made from hollowed-out tree trunks. They must have lived in straw or reed huts quite near their heaps of shell-fish, in which they often buried their dead; the bodies were generally doubled up.

Beneath the big tree on the right of this scene are two small straw huts, side by side, on the roofs of which skulls of Deer, Bear and wild Boar have been placed as trophies. Before the huts, two mothers welcome their Menfolk on their return from the daily fishing and hunting expeditions. An enormous Sea-Pike has been caught, no doubt with a harpoon having tiny stone barbs. Fishing with a line and fish-hook and deep sea fishing must both have been practised. Two children on the extreme left are busy with their lines, and a Man in the centre foreground is mending the flint barbs of his harpoon, re-sharpening some and replacing others. One of the Dogs barks at the monster fish, while another nurses her puppies and growls at the child who wants to touch them. Having collected the big basketful of shells in front of the left-hand hut as well as a large Crab, three young Women dance near their little children, their castanets probably being flat pieces of bone like the Africans use.

On the opposite bank a canoe is being hauled ashore near a second village of four huts, which is separated from the first by an arm of the river. Chestnut and cork trees and parasol pines grow on the lower ancient terraces of the Tagus; in the distance are the hills of Pliocene and Cretaceous date, backed by the granite highlands. An Eagle hovers, Swans are flying and Ducks splash in the water. There is a blue Thrush and Magpies and Squirrels play in the chestnut trees, not at all frightened by the people below.

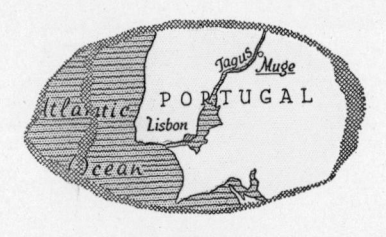

GLACIATIONS AND HUMAN INDUSTRIES AND RACES IN EUROPE

GLACIAL AND INTERGLACIAL LEVELS	INDUSTRIES ON ROUGH FLAKES	BIFACED INDUSTRIES (Tools worked on both faces)	INDUSTRY WITH WIDE, VERY OBLIQUE STRIKING PLATFORMS	FLAKE INDUSTRIES: STRIKING PLATFORMS PREPARED ON CORES. (Little Secondary Trimming)	FLAKE INDUSTRIES: STRIKING PLATFORMS PREPARED ON CORES. (Flakes Smaller and Much Retrimmed)	UPPER PALEO-LITHIC AND MESOLITHIC	RACES
PRE-GÜNZ AND GÜNZ-GLACIAL	FLAKES FROM BENEATH THE IPSWICH THE RED CRAG, AND ITS UPPER LEVEL	(a) WORK-SHOP OF THE CROMER BEACH (PERHAPS OLD ABBE-VILLIAN)					
INTERGLACIAL GÜNZ-MINDEL		(b) ALL THE SUBDIVISIONS OF THE ABBEVILLIAN INDUSTRY					MAUER. HOMO PRE-NEANDERTHAL.
GLACIAL MINDEL		(c) BASE OF THE CLAC-TONIAN INDUSTRY					
INTERGLACIAL MINDEL-RISS	THE PRECEDING INDUSTRIES ARE CRUSHED IN THE MINDEL GLACIAL DEPOSITS						
		ACHEU-LEAN { Lower / Middle / Upper }	(a) MID-CLACTONIAN OF CLACTON AND EVOLVED OF HIGH LODGE — LOWER TAYACIAN				PILTDOWN HOMO PRE-SAPIENS SWANSCOMBE
GLACIAL RISS				(c) LEVALLOISIAN I, II and IIIA			
INTERGLACIAL RISS-WURM	THE PRECEDING INDUSTRIES ARE CRUSHED IN THE RISSIAN GLACIAL DEPOSITS	FINAL ACHEULEAN OR MICOQUIAN — The bifaced industries of ACHEULEAN tradition are found in many more recent LEVALLOISIAN and MOUSTERIAN levels (EXAMPLE: COMBE CAPELLE: upper level LA QUINA)	MID-TAYACIAN UPPER MICOQUE evolving towards MOUSTERIAN — The latest MOUSTERIAN SITES still show this manner of chipping stone (EXAMPLE: base of LA ROCHETTE; LA QUINA).	LEVALLOISIAN IIIB and IV			NEANDERTHAL
GLACIAL WURM I				LEVALLOIS V	MOUSTERIAN WEIMAR TYPE ANCIENT MOUSTERIAN LEVELS IN CAVES		
MILDER PERIOD				LEVALLOIS VI and VII	MOUSTERIAN — These Industries are mixed with ACHEULEAN, LEVALLOISIAN and CLACTONIAN types.	AURIGNACIAN	HOMO SAPIENS
GLACIAL WURM II						SOLUTREAN LOWER MAGDALENIAN UPPER MAGDALENIAN	COMBE-CAPELLE CRO-MAGNON GRIMALDI, etc.
POST-WURM PRESENT CLIMATE						AZILIAN MAGLEMOSIAN TARDENOISIAN	PRESENT DAY RACES HOMO SAPIENS

NOTE : INDUSTRY is the name given to the outfit of stone tools used by prehistoric Man at a given period ; thus—"Magda-lenian industry"—the tools used by Magdalenian Man whose remains were first found at La Madeleine, Dordogne.

INDEX

NOTE: For Lists of Illustrations see pages 10 and 34.

A

ABBEVILLE, 12, 18, 28
ABBEVILLIAN INDUSTRY, 18, 38
ACHEULEAN INDUSTRY, 18
AFRICA, South-West, 19
AGRICULTURE, birth of, 26
AISNE, department of, 18
ALBACETE, 83
ALMERIA, 83
ALPÉRA, 83
ALTAMIRA, cave of, 16
ANDRÉ, Paul, 11
ANEMONE, furry, 66
ANTELOPE, 38
ANTLER, tools from, 57
ANVIL, 54, 55
APE, 21
AQUITAINE, 19
ARIÈGE, 16, 18, 25, 29, 79, 82
——, map, 82
ARISE, river, 88
Aromia Moschata (beetle), 11
ARROW, 55, 91
ASIA, 21, 47
ASS, wild, 38
ASTURIAS, 87
ASTURIAN TOOLS, 87
ATHABASKA, Indians, 63
AURIGNAC, site of, 12, 18
AURIGNACIAN MAN, 51
—— Sculpture, 72
AWL, 54, 71
AXE, dolerite fashioning of, 41
AZILIAN MAN, 18, 88

B

BADEN, 22
BALTIC, glacier, 91
BARBATE, river, 72
BASKET, 83
BATRACIANS, age of, 19
BEAR, hunting, 22, 42, 43, 50, 58, 59, 65, 90
——, cave, 73
——, clay model, 80, 82
BEAVER, 92
BEES, wild, 83

BEGOUEN Count, sons of, 16
BELGIUM, 73
BEUNE, river, 47, 66
BISON, hunting, 43, 65, 77
——, skull of, 90
BLANGY, 12
BOAR, wild, 83, 88, 90, 92, 93
BOIS DE ROCHER, 75
BONE, use of, 55
BORDEAUX, 73
BOUCHER DE PERTHES, 28
BOUILLANCOURT - EN - SERY, castle, 12
BOW, 87, 91
BRANDBERG, mountains, 19
BURIAL, Magdalenian, 71
BURIN, 54, 55, 57
BURKITT, Miles, 30

C

CABO DA ROCA, 86, 87
CADIZ, province, 72
Calosoma Inquisitor (beetle), 11
CANADA, 92
CANTABRIA, 19
CAP BLANC, rock shelter, 66, 71
CAPE PROVINCE, 16
CARTAILHAC, Emile, 32
CASTANETS, 93
CASTILE, 83
CATALONIA, 83
CATERPILLARS, 11
CATTLE, wild, 71, 72, 93
CÈPES (mushrooms), 47
CERITH, 75
CERITHIUM, giant, 11
——, silicified, 12
CERNUNNOS, 82
Cervus Megaceros, 35, 37, 38, 47
CHAMOIS, 65
CHANCELADE, 71
CHARENTE, department of, 43, 66
——, map, 43, 75
——, river, 75
CHESTNUT (tree), 93
CHIMPANZEE, 21, 22

CHOPPER, 39
CHOUGH (*Pyrrhoeorax*), 38
CHOU-KOU-TIEN, bone brecchia of, 18
—— ——, map, 38
—— ——, site, 20, 35, 36, 37
CHUKCHI, salmon-eating, 60
"CHURINGA," 90
CLACTONIAN INDUSTRY, 18
CLEAVERS, 39, 41
CLERMONT, 11
CLIMATE, change of, 21, 26
CLUB, 39, 42, 65
——, wooden, 54
Clytia, 11
COLLÈGE DE FRANCE, 11
COMARQUE, castle, 66
CONYERS, 28
CORE, flint, 54, 57
CORK (tree), 93
CRO-DU-CHARNIER, 23, 55
CRO-MAGNON, 75
CUISE (Oise), 73
CYPREA, 75

D

D'AULT DE MESNIL, *see* MESNIL
DAGGER, 71
DAUPHINÉ, 65
DEER, fallow, 47, 83
——, red, 91
DESMONDVILLE, Museum, 12
DEVIMEUX, 11
DOG, 90, 93
DOLERITE, tools of, 41
DORDOGNE, 18, 43, 47
——, map, 51, 66
DRYOPITHECUS (ape), 21
DUCK, 38, 87, 93

E

EAGLE, 61, 66, 93
EASTERN SPAIN, Art of, 15, 83

Elephas Antiquus, 39
Elater Sanguineus, 11
ELEPHANT, fossil bones of, 26, 39
——, Mammoth, 38
ELK, Irish, 51, 82, 83, 88, 91, 92
ENGLAND, 18
EOCENE LIMESTONE, 11
ESKIMO, salmon-eating, 60
—— dress, 63
—— way of living, 79
EUROPE, extension of ice, 22
——, prehistoric civilizations, 18, 26
EVANS, John, 28

F

FALCONER, 28
FIRE, early use, 28
—— making, 36, 39
FISH, age of, 19
FLAKE, flint, 54
FLINT, chipping, 38, 41, 54
—— tools, 66
FONT-DE-GAUME, 47, 51
FOX, 93
FRANCE, 18, 55, 90, 92
FRERE, John, 28
FUNERAL CEREMONY, 71

G

GALILEO, 9
GARONNE, river, 16
GAZELLE, 35, 38
GENTIAN, 66
GEOMETRIC DESIGN, 90
GERMANY, 22
GIBRALTAR, straits of, 91
" GOD," of Trois Frères cave, 82, 83
GORILLA, 21
GRASSET, Dr., 15

GRIGNON (Seine et Oise), 73
GRIMALDI, 71, 75

H

HANDS, painted, 73
HARE, mountain, 59
HARPOON, barbs, points, 57, 61, 80, 90, 93
HAUTE GARONNE, department of, 80
HERON, 38
HIPPOPOTAMUS, 41
Homo Sapiens, 55
HORSE, wild, as food, 22, 50, 51, 57
——, bone tools, 57
——, sculptured, 69, 80
HOXNE, 28
HUNTING DISGUISES, 23, 77
HYAENA, 38, 43, 61

I

IBEX, 65, 66, 80, 83, 90
INDIA, 21
INITIATION CEREMONY, 83
INSECTS, study of, 11

J

JAVA, 21, 35
JAVELIN, 43, 55, 66
JUDAS TREE, 37

K

KUDU (antelope), 41

L

LADYBRAND, O.F.S., 19
LA-FÈRE-EN-TARDENOIS, 18
LA MADELEINE, 18, 61

LAMP, 79
LANCE, bone point, 73
LA PILETA, 18
LARTET, Edouard, 18
LA ROCHEFOUCAULD, 75
LASCAUX, cave of, 16, 23
LAUREL-LEAF (point), 54, 55
LAUSSEL, castle, 66
LAVAL, 16
LE MOUSTIER, 18
LEMUR, 21
LE PLACARD, 75
LES EYZIES, 47, 71
—— ——, map, 66
LEVALLOIS FLAKE, 12
——, site, 18
LEVALLOISIAN INDUSTRY, 18
LIMOUSIN, 63
LION, 50, 51, 59, 69, 73, 90
LISBON, 15
LOT, department of, 58
LOUVRIÉ, Justin, 13
LUTETIAN LEVEL, 12
LYELL, Charles, 28
LYNX, 71, 93

M

Machairodus (tiger), 37
MACON, 55
MAESTRAZYGO (Castellón), 83
MAGDALENIAN INDUSTRY, 18
—— MAN, 51, 57, 58, 59, 61
MAGIC, ceremonies, 79, 80, 83
MAGLEMOSIAN PERIOD, 91
MAGPIE, 93
MAKAPAN CAVE, bone brecchia, 18
MALAGA, 18
MAMMALS, age of, 19, 21
MAMMOTH, hunting, 22, 43, 47, 51, 73
MAN, age of, 19
——, Ipswich, 8
——, Java, 8, 21
——, Neanderthal, 22, 42, 47, 55

MAN, PEKIN, 8, 20, 21
——, PILTDOWN, 22
MARMOT, 65, 77
MARSAL, 16
MARSOULAS, cave of, 90
MARTAGON LILY, 66
MAS D'AZIL, cave of, 18, 28, 82, 88
MAUER, human remains at, 22
MENTONE, caves at, 75
MESNIL, d'Ault de, 12
MESOLITHIC AGE, 87, 88, 91, 92
MINHO, river, 87
MONTESPAN, clay bear of, 80
MONTESQUIEU - AVANTÈS, 25, 27, 79
MONTIGNAC (Dordogne), 16
MOOSE, 92
MORAVIA, 73
MOROCCO, 16
MOUSTERIAN HUNTING, 43, 47, 50
MUGE (Mugem), 93
MUREX, 75
MUSHROOM, Cêpe, 47
——, Chanterelle, 47
——, Girolle, 47
——, intoxication by, 47

N

NARCISSUS, 66
NEANDERTHAL MAN, 22, 42, 47, 55
NEEDLE, 57
NESLE, 12
Névé (melting snow), 66
NIAUX, 18

O

OCHRE, red, 22, 68, 69, 78
——, grinding, 77
ORANGE FREE STATE, 19
OSTRICH, 38

OTTER, 92
OXEN, wild, 93

P

PAINTING, 73, 77, 78, 83
——, colours for, 68
PALETTE, 68
PALUDISM, 93
PANTHER, 47, 59, 71
Papilio Machaon, 11
PARIS, 18
PEBBLE, painted, 88
PECTEN (shell), 75, 78
PEERS CAVE, Fishhoek, 17
PEKIN MAN, 20, 21, 35, 36, 37
PERCUSSION, bi-polar, 35
——, manual, 41
PÉRIGORD, 42, 50, 72, 77, 78
PÉRIGORDIANS, 51
PICARDY, 12
PIETTE, Edouard, 88
PILTDOWN MAN, 22
Pithecanthropus (Java), 35
PLANTAUREL, mountains, 88
POLISHING TOOLS, 57
PORTUGAL, 16, 86
PREHISTORY, science of, 7, 8, 9, 11, 18
PRESSIGNY, knives, 12
PRESSURE FLAKING, 55
PRESTWICK, 28
PRIVET HAWK MOTH, 11
Pseudaxis (deer), 37
PUNCH (tool), 71
PUSS MOTH, 11
PYRENEES, 91

R

RAVIDAT, 16
RAYMONDEN, 71
REINDEER, sculptured, 43, 80
——, meat in grave, 71
——, painting, 77
——, use of antler, 55

REINDEER, AGE, art, 13
—— ——, hunters, 50, 90
—— ——, hunting, 22, 63, 77
REPTILE AGE, 19, 21
RHINOCEROS, woolly, 38, 41, 43, 47, 51, 73, 83
RHODODENDRON, 66
ROCHEBERTIER, 75
ROSE COTTAGE, Cave, 19
RUSTENBURG, 15

S

SAINT ACHEUL, 18
—— GAUDENS, 80
—— MÉDARD, gravels, 12
—— SULPICE, garden, 14
SALAT, river, 90
SALMON RUNNING, 60, 61
SANCTUARY, of Trois Frères, 79, 80, 82, 83
SANTANDER, 16
SAÔNE ET LOIRE, 18, 54, 55
SAUTUOLA, Marcelin de, 16
SCANDINAVIA, 91, 92
SCRAPER, side, 54, 57
SCULPTOR, at Cap Blanc, 66
——, Aurignacian, 72
SEAL, 93
SERS, valley du Roc, 66
SHELLS, commerce in, 73, 75
SHELL-FISH, 84, 87, 92
SHREW AGE, 21
SIERRA DE SINTRA, 84
Sinanthropus (Pekin Man), 37, 38
SIWALIK hills, 21
SKINS, preparation of, 57
SNAILS, 88
SOISSONAIS, 11, 12
SOLUTRE, site, 18, 23, 51, 54, 71
SOLUTREAN INDUSTRY, 18
SOMME, river, 16
——, basin, 38
——, department, 18
SOUTH AFRICA, 15
SORCERER, 66

SPAIN, Eastern, 16, 58, 83
Spiroceros, 38
SQUIRREL, 59, 93
STATUETTES, earliest, 22
STORK, 59
SUSSEX (Piltdown), 22
SWALLOW, 38
SWALLOW-TAIL (butterfly), 11
SWAN, 43, 59, 93
SWIFT, 90

T

TAGUS, 92, 93
TARDENOISEAN INDUSTRY, 18
TARDOIRE, valley, 75
TAYAC, site, 18
TAYACIAN INDUSTRY, 18
THAMES, flint chipping, 16, 38
THROWING-STICKS, 66
THRUSH, blue, 93
TOADSTOOLS, edible, 47
TRANSVAAL, 18

TROIS FRÈRES, cave of, 16, 18, 27, 79, 80, 82, 83
TUC D'AUDOUBERT, cave of, 16, 24, 79, 80
TUNGUS, salmon-eaters, 60
TURRITELLA, 75

U

UPPER AURIGNACIAN Times, 51
UPPER PALAEOLITHIC Circus, 58
——— Man, 47, 65, 87
——— Times, 54, 55, 57
——— Trade, 73

V

VAAL, river, 16, 41
———, map, 41
———, stone tools, 41

VERCORS (Dauphiné), 65
VÉZÈRE, river, 47, 51, 57, 61, 66
VILHONNEUR, 75
VOLP, river, 24, 79
VULTURE, 38

W

WEAPONS, early, 22
WILLOW-LEAVES (tools), 54
WITWATERSRAND UNIVERSITY, 19
WOLVES, 38, 43, 50, 51, 58, 59, 61, 63, 69, 77

Z

ZEBU, 71

GLOSSARY

AMMONITE	.. ..	Extinct marine animal with shell like ram's horn.
AMULET ..	.. ..	Object worn as protection against evil, or bad luck.
ANTI-CLINAL	.. ..	Forming a ridge so that the earth's strata lean against each other.
AQUITAINE	.. ..	District of France south of the Loire and west of the Allier rivers.
BATRACIAN	.. ..	Animal that can live on land and in water.
BELEMNITE	.. ..	Fossil shaped like end of a dart.
BIFACED TOOL	.. ..	Tool trimmed on both faces.
BRECCHIA		Mass of small pieces of rock held together by natural cement.
BURIN	.. ..	Pointed tool used by engravers.
CERITHIUM	.. ..	Turret-shaped fossil shell.
CLEAVER ..	.. ..	Cutting tool for hewing or splitting.
COLEOPTERA	.. ..	Beetles in which front wings sheath hind wings when folded.
CRETACEOUS	.. ..	Latest stage of Secondary Age, when England was submerged.
ENTOMOLOGIST..	.. ..	Student and classifier of insects.
EOCENE LIMESTONE	..	Made in first period of Tertiary Age when England was part of Continent.
FOSSIL MAN	.. ..	Types of men living before written history.
GLACIAL PERIOD	.. ..	Age when country was covered by ice.
GUNZ	.. ..	Name given to an ice age in Europe
ICHTHYOSAURUS	..	Extinct fish-like reptile.
INTERGLACIAL PERIOD		Time of milder climate between two ice ages.
JAVELIN	.. ..	Light spear.
LEVALLOIS FLAKE	..	Method of trimming stone flake tool used at Levallois, France.
LIMOUSIN	.. ..	Part of the Dept. of Haute Vienne, France.
LOWER PALÆOLITHIC MAN		Man living in the Old Stone Age.
LUTETIAN LEVEL	..	Level of soil near Paris (*from* Lutetia, old name of city).
MAGLEMOSIAN ..		Phase of the Mesolithic period (*from* Maglemose, Zealand, Denmark).
MAMMOTH	.. ..	Extinct elephant with heavy woolly coat and up-curved tusks, that lived in Europe.
MESOLITHIC AGE	..	Period following Late Stone Age.
MINDEL ..	.. ..	Name given to an ice age in Europe.
MOUSTERIAN ..		Middle Old Stone Age.
NEOLITHIC AGE	..	New Stone Age when agriculture was begun and animals were tamed and herded.
OSTEOLOGY	.. ..	Study of bones, their development and structure.
PALÆONTOLOGY	..	Science of Fossils.
PLESIOSAURUS ..		Extinct marine reptile with long neck and 4 limbs used as paddles when swimming.
PLIOCENE ..	.. ..	Third state of Tertiary Age when soil called ''Red crag'' was formed.
RISS ..	.. ..	Name given to an ice age in Europe.
SILICIFIED	.. ..	Highly glazed by silica.
TINE	.. ..	Prong of deer antler.
UPPER PALÆOLITHIC MAN	..	Man living in the later Old Stone Age.
WURM	.. ..	Name given to an ice age in Europe.